CHICAGO STORYTELLERS FROM STAGE TO PAGE

Edited by Judi Lee Goshen
& Anne E. Beall, PhD
Foreword by Jill Howe

Chicago Story Press, Inc.

ISBN-978-0-578-80628-0

Cover design by: Wilson Piechazek

*In Loving Memory of
Tom Wolferman*

CONTENTS

INTRODUCTION

We love storytelling! We love stories because we believe they are the road maps that we use to navigate our lives. That is undoubtedly the reason why stories have been a part of every human culture. The best stories are instructive, amusing, and emotionally evocative. Stories instruct us about what to do (and what not to do), how to handle difficult situations and people, and how to manage our emotions. Stories are one of the great tools we have in our life toolbox, which is why they have such staying power. You always remember a good story and how it made you feel. Stories also reveal a lot about a storyteller and are a shortcut into someone's heart and soul. Stories are powerful.

We have been part of the Chicago storytelling community for many years and have had the great privilege of hearing the best tellers in the city. One of those people was Tom Wolferman, who engaged many audiences with his dry, acerbic wit. His delivery was always deadpan, and you would laugh inwardly for several minutes at his turns of phrase. When he passed away unexpectedly, we lost a Chicago treasure. We also lost a wonderful friend.

The goal of this volume was to collect great tellers from Chicago into one volume so they can live forever within these pages and can be enjoyed repeatedly. We also wanted to share our renowned tellers with those who may not make it to Chicago any time soon. We have compiled a wide range of meaningful, poignant stories from childhood to middle age, that cover everything from race relations to family relations. Some are funny and others are heartwarming. All are lovely and are written by tellers who have performed on stage in Chicago.

We're delighted to share these stories with you, particularly during these trying times, when most of us are social distancing. So sit back, grab a drink, and enjoy the storytellers that have gone from stage to page.

—Anne & Judi

P.S. Everyone has a story. Feel free to submit yours to: Hello@ChicagoStoryPress.com

www.chicagostorypress.com

FOREWORD BY JILL HOWE

About fifty years ago, a storytelling rumbling started and it spread. It wasn't the origin of storytelling. No, that had been going on all the way back to Appalachia, and probably the cave-dwellers. Festivals popped up, regional shows splintered further, and a final explosion occurred in the cities. Radio and podcast hosts eventually picked up on storytelling and broadcast it to the masses. They wanted more laughs, more cries, more shame, more guilt, more redemption, more stark truths, and more stories.

In my early thirties I fell absolutely head over heels in love with live storytelling in Chicago. People were standing before an audience telling the truth, making the worst things hilarious or heartfelt, and weaving stories with dazzling structure and sublime endings. I wanted more and more! I took so many classes. However, my early thirties' bank account couldn't quite keep up with the expensive workshops I craved. When I started storytelling, I didn't know how to speak into a mic, and I was so anxious that I would practically black out after telling a story! I had to ask my friends in the audience if I had indeed told a story.

I had to find a better way. What if I just started inviting the most impressive storytellers over to my living room? And then what if I kept adding people? I gave it a name ... Friends with Words (FWW), always friendship before the critique. Feedback can be a nasty experience with the wrong group, and my job became that of a story shepherd. I found the spaces in people's homes (I am excellent at throwing a party in *your* home), I set the tone, I moderated the time, and I provided ample time for friend-ships to form. What happened next would be the happiest sur-prise of my life: I made a family. After almost a decade of monthly gatherings, the group has changed over the years, continually morphing to fit the artistic needs of those present, those who come to come to share stories, and those who want to just listen that month. I count every member among my most respected and beloved friends.

Anne Beall and Judi Lee Goshen, your editors for this wonderful compilation, met in Friends with Words. We often remark on how the tiniest choices to go to a show or not can define your future best friendships. As is the case with Friends with Words, it often comes back to my relentless befriending of artists and dragging them into my collection of talent. *Everyone say hi! Now sit here. Begin. Tell us your story.* Anne and Judi have come almost every month of the eight years and have formed a story bond that is beautiful, cooperative, and impeccably creative. As published authors, they know the discipline of writing and the joy of sharing. They've wholeheartedly embraced vulnerability and have brought such depth and kindness to FWW.

I grew so drunk with the connectivity of it all that I started producing my own show, Story Sessions. I took everyone along for the ride, including Anne and Judi, who held on tight and supported my work. Story Sessions began in the back room of a bar long gone called the Dog's Bollox, I know, what a name! Against all odds, the *Chicago Tribune* came and reported that our only problem was that we didn't have enough seating. That was in 2013, and I haven't stopped. I don't think I will ever be able to. When a book like this one can come into the world because of our connections, imagine the impact stories can have in the world. Our narratives are our future.

The first time I heard Tom Wolferman tell a story in the back room of a bar, I found myself cracking up over his neurotic antics about a movie theater bully. I risked being perceived as weird and promptly introduced myself to him and invited him to my group, FWW. Month after month, Tom would take our breath away with his sharp wit, charming self-deprecation, and heartfelt vulnerabilities. Most performers relish that last "headliner" position in the lineup, but not Tom. Tom wanted to go first, to "get the damn thing over with!" And so Tom, a reluctant center stage, always began the FWW session.

I was shopping for roses one night when I got a message from a friend, "Sorry to hear about your friend Tom." I hurriedly typed back that I was confused and learned that Tom was gone. It all happened so shockingly fast. I stared at the dozen red roses in my arms. I just stared and stared. And then burst into tears right there in the store. I haven't bought red roses since, and I will remain inconsolable over the loss of my brave heart, my strongest support, the gift of a true artistic colleague. Tom, of all the artists I have ever known, should have been published while he was alive. I believe he would have been in print soon had he stayed with us a little longer. This collection of essays is a tribute to him and to the brave tellers who choose to bare their souls, reach out into the unknown, take the stage, and connect. As you will see with this collection, stories that shine on stage can also soar on the page. Now if you'll wrap a blanket around you tight, Tom Wolferman will start the show.

Jill Howe is the producer of *Story Sessions*, a showcase featuring true stories and live music. Jill has facilitated her monthly storytelling group *Friends with Words* for the last eight years, she organizes and teaches *Story Sessions* writing retreats, and she has presented a Tedx Talk on vulnerability through storytelling. She shares her stories at bars and theaters all around Chicagoland. She also recently became a resident storyteller at The Field Museum, where she develops kid-friendly true stories about beloved animals who need to have their memories dusted off.

CHAPTER 1: FIFTY SHADES OF BEIGE BY TOM WOLFERMAN

I am sitting in a movie theater about to watch Jennifer Aniston's descent into Bummertown. A film called *Cake*. And I'm thinking, on this cold, lifeless January night, I'd rather be eating cake. Better still, I could really go for some pie. Instead, my momentary distraction is interrupted by a preview trailer with inane dialogue: "I don't do romance. My tastes are very singular. You wouldn't understand."

A shirtless guy stands in front of the world's most organized closet. A row of perfectly aligned crisp white shirts and fitted suits are meticulously hung at three-inch intervals. He opens a drawer of neckties, each folded in individual compartments. Eventually, he removes blindfolds from another perfectly organized drawer. The quick cuts are interspersed with more dim-witted proclamations.

"I exercise control in all things."

If not for the kinky interludes with ice cubes and restraints, I'd be convinced I am watching a haunting promotion for The Container Store's Annual 30% Off Elfa Shelving Sale. Although I'm confused why they would score it with a provocative Beyoncé soundtrack.

Of course, I am watching a trailer for *Fifty Shades of Grey*. I know it's designed to whip its target audience into a frenzy of sadomasochistic longing, but within *me* it awakens a deep, pulsating yearning to get better organized. I want to flee the theater immediately so I can alphabetize my socks and set up a Dewey Decimal System to keep tabs on my earmuffs.

Mostly, watching this montage of brain-dead slapstick

leads me to believe these people have never lived through a Chicago winter—which is known to be sadomasochistic but rarely erotic. We are too exhausted being pummeled by the elements to slap each other around in the name of love. Then again, all bets are off if someone steals your parking space.

In the dead of February, nothing is sexy. Definitely not the ratty tan parka I've worn for the past ten years exclusively for snow removal. I am living Fifty Shades of Beige. It is a bland, colorless struggle for survival. And I can't muster the strength for an erotic awakening until I see the first signs of a Marshmallow Peep.

It's not that I don't have fantasies. Every December 1, once Chicago's overnight winter parking ban goes into effect, I cling to the illusion. *It's not so bad. Only four months or so. I'll focus on indoor things. Like recaulking the bathroom and attempting to get through the first chapter of* One Hundred Years of Solitude. But once the soft-baked gingerbread of December goes stale, all that's left are the brittle frozen crumbs of January. I am disciplined by the weather. I am dominated by Eddie Bauer. And, yes, I am the bitch-slapped subservient to ABC-TV weekend meteorologist Phil Schwarz.

In what is supposed to be a racy foreshadowing scene from the movie, the dominant protagonist, doing some light shopping to furnish his Red Room of Pain, hits on the passive object of his desire—a lit major who happens to work part-time at a hardware store. Apparently in Housewares and Domestic Punishment. "Do you stock cable ties? Masking tape? Rope?" he asks flirtatiously. I had a similar experience last week when I stalked the aisles of Home Depot to purchase the ten-count value pack of HotHands winter hand warmers. Because the packaging promised a total of up to 200 hours of heat, I was feeling so erogenous I loitered around the Home Depot hot dog kiosk, hoping to satisfy my cravings for pleasure and pain.

Although I'd like to jump on the trend, I have concerns that I may be too practical for a BDSM relationship. I once rented the film *9-1/2 Weeks,* which coincidentally is exactly how long it takes to shovel out my alley. In an iconic scene, Mickey

Rourke, who back then still looked like Mickey Rourke, orders Kim Basinger to keep her eyes closed as she obediently samples contents from his refrigerator. I've never tried this at home because there's nothing sensual about force-feeding a potential love interest broccoli crowns and a week-old half-eaten burrito from Chipotle. In fact, if I ever found myself hosting someone submissively crouched in front of my fridge, I wouldn't squander the opportunity on foreplay. I would hand them a spray bottle of Fantastic and a no-scratch sponge and demand that they go to town. Then we'd move on to the tub until it sparkled.

By now maybe some of you are thinking, "Hey Tom, I'm beige too. How can I get my sexy groove back and survive winter without the bother of handcuffing someone to a rickety headboard?"

As a public service, I'm here to help. To guide you through the remaining cold and desperate hours. To tell you that by spicing up your everyday encounters with poorly written erotic dialogue, you can dial up the heat from a dreary shade of beige to a red-hot taupe.

Let's imagine you're checking out at Trader Joe's. Following required employee protocol, the chirpy clerk asks if you found everything you were looking for. Don't hold back:

"The insatiable longings deep within my famished tenderloins can only be fed by free-range turkey waffles, pumpkin-infused hummus, and a savory bag of peppermint-encrusted kale chips."

And suppose you're commuting on Chicago public transportation, possibly the Red Line of Pain. You just want to read, but the guy seated next to you is encroaching on your personal space with excessive manspreading. Don't dismiss him. He could be solid relationship material after you lean in and whisper, "Hey, Magic Mike. I've got a loaded Ventra Card that can take us past Chinatown and all the way to paradise."

Or maybe you've been summoned to jury duty. And whose heart doesn't pound with excitement over the thought of venturing to the Criminal Courts Building in the middle of a light wintry mix? But due to urgent commitments, which involve the binge-watching of *Game of Thrones* and *The Mentalist*, you can't possibly serve. When the judge inquires how you feel about a two-week felony trial, just get all hot and swampy Tennessee Williams:

"How do I feel? How do I feel, your honor? I feel all the time like a cat on a hot tin roof!" Juror excused.

Finally, you return to your Chicago side street, which even the Mars Rover wouldn't attempt to navigate, and find someone has parked in the spot you passionately shoveled out. Why expend negative energy on puncturing someone's tires when you can establish a potent relationship with a consensual agreement affixed to their windshield?

Attention you who have dibs on my heart. Please sign the attached contract of consent so that I may smack your round, ample, lethargic ass so hard it won't be able to sit in the obsolete patio furniture I salvaged to save this spot.

All this Fifty Shades of Hype makes me realize I have a love-hate relationship with this city. It's that time of year when you realize you've been hunched over for three months and every passerby is telepathically asking each other the same question: "Why do we live here?"

And then you remember that hidden storefront theater, that bakery with real scones, the indie bookstore that has the audacity to exist, and all the people you love who are in deep, alongside you, in this maddening urban pothole. And you know with that first warm hopeful swipe of May, you will forget the pain.

But meanwhile, the summer solstice is 119 days away, and according to my calculations, I've got less than 150 hours of heat left in my hand warmers. I need to conserve energy. So instead of recreational spanking, flogging, and whipping, how about if we just go out for some pie?

Tom Wolferman followed a lifelong writing path that was interesting, eclectic, and unpredictable. Navigating a balancing act where creativity was often at odds with commerce, he wrote advertising copy, employee communications, the occasional humor piece for the *Chicago Tribune* and *Chicago Reader,* and fun-filled oxymoronic projects involving corporate comedy.

He was a beloved member of Chicago's storytelling community and was a featured teller at Story Sessions, Story Club, Story Lab, and Essay Fiesta.

He was an integral member of the Chicago writing group Friends with Words. Tom passed away unexpectedly in 2018 and is sorely missed.

CHAPTER 2: CUPCAKE BY LINDSEY MONROE-BOUGHER

In fifth grade, I was the amazing, remarkable invisible girl. My invisibility was surprising, considering that in the '80s I wore a mixture of '70s hand-me-downs from my gaggle of female cousins and the few trendy neon shirts that my mom bought me. Neither of these styles lent themselves well toward hiding the wearer, but I was adept at fading into the wallpaper.

I had a terrible perm, gigantic plastic glasses, and the most awkward manner of any ten-year-old girl in the world. That sounds hyperbolic, but a panel of leading experts agreed: I was the worst. I didn't know how to talk to my peers. I was so afraid to say the wrong thing that I either sank into a choking silence or spat out a rapid, meaningless patter. I did well with adults, but that only reduced my standing. I was oblivious and convinced that I only needed to get my foot in the door of the popular crowd.

I may have been the queen of the undesirables, but I was an excellent reader. I read constantly. It was the only thing that ever earned me a reprimand from a teacher. The problem with my escape into books was that I started trying to apply the Laws of Fiction to real life.

Fiction Law #1: Very shy girls will be picked as a best-friend foil to an outgoing girl. Do not fight your shyness. Just place yourself near the popular girls, so you are available when it's time for them to select their shy friend. Stare at them blatantly, so they know you would like to be considered. They may seem uncomfortable, but do not be deterred! Awkwardness is part of the process.

Fiction Law #2: Very shy girls will likely be tasked with an adventure or quest of some kind. Don't be surprised when an elf appears and begs you to rescue their kingdom! This type of request is to be expected, and you should be ready to jump through a portal to assist at any time. Any quest regarding treasure must be accepted immediately.

Fiction Law #3: Boys appreciate a direct approach. (This may be true later in life, but rings false for ten-year-olds.) If you, a very shy girl, have a crush on a boy and want to be his girlfriend, it would be best if you approach the boy and ask him. This is not a question that would seem weird to a normal child. When they sidle away, it's a sign of admiration for your courage. Romance is always just around the corner for very shy fifth graders. Be ready for it!

Following these rules, I was able to achieve a level of dork-i-tude that put me squarely in between the unfortunate kids who were actively picked on and the smart kids who were cool enough to be included. That invisible no-man's-land allowed me to be friends with a big group of girls, and still manage to get left out much of the time. Most likely, I was allowed into their established friend-group simply because they couldn't shake me. I haunted their steps like a private eye in a noir film, replacing a hip flask of rye with a Capri Sun and a packet of Fun Dip.

A few weeks before Valentine's Day, one of the classes in my school announced that they would be selling cupcakes for the big day. For a quarter you could pick a recipient, write them a note, and it would be delivered along with a cupcake on Valentine's Day. Of course, the delivery would be done during class, to make sure that everyone could witness the happiness or heartbreak of their classmates. It was one of the seasoning processes of youth that helped us to develop either a positive outlook on life or a deep and abiding cynicism.

As a shy girl who firmly believed in the Laws of Fiction, rather than the harsh lessons elementary school had so far dealt to her, I began preparing myself for a wonderful Valentine's Day. My vision for the day was beautiful. I imagined myself receiving cupcake after cupcake. Some of them would be from my friends. The notes would tell me how much fun I was to be around, and how glad they were to be friends with me. Some of them would be from the boys who inevitably fell to my charms, swept off their feet by my winsome smile and French-rolled jeans. My teacher would be amazed! All my friends would hold their breath, hoping to get cupcakes from me as well. I could not disappoint them! This would take some work.

At that time, I got one dollar per week for my allowance. It was an embarrassment of riches, but it didn't provide enough capital to buy cupcakes for everyone on my list. Thus I began my treasure-hunting campaign. My sisters and I walked about a mile and a half to school, so there was a lot of ground to cover. I checked in the gutters and streets, in the shallow water near the creek, and in the parking lot of the apartments near the school. I checked all the couch cushions in my house, and pestered my folks in case they were feeling generous. They were not.

After all the scrimping, saving, and panhandling, I was able to buy cupcakes for all my friends. I did it secretly, of course, because I wanted them to be surprised. I was so excited that I could barely contain myself! As Valentine's Day approached, I readied myself for the avalanche of cake and acceptance.

When the day finally arrived, I wanted to look my best and most festive. I wore my red sweatshirt and heart earrings. I put on a sickening amount of cherry ChapStick, the closest thing to makeup I was allowed. I was ready for my moment in the spotlight.

I set my valentine box on the front of my desk in preparation for the exchange. I loved giving and receiving cards and candy from the whole class. I knew we were all required to bring cards for everyone, but it made me feel like one of the gang anyway. It certainly didn't matter that the overwhelming majority of cards I received had nothing personal written in them. They took the time to write my name, after all. The cupcakes, however, were so much more important to me, because nobody had to get one for me. They would be doing it because they wanted to do it.

I had a thrilling chill running up my back in anticipation, and the first time the door opened for the cupcake cart I tried hard to play it cool.

There were none for me in the first batch. I wasn't worried, because the deliveries would be going on for a while. The second and third time the door opened, I still expected them to come to my desk. I wouldn't admit to myself that I was disappointed. I hung on to hope for a very long time before the truth set in. Time after time, the door opened, and a cupcake would be given to someone else. My friends received the cupcakes I sent them, as well as the ones they sent to each other. My desk remained empty.

One important Law of Fiction is that the very shy girl must be brave enough to fight back her tears. I tried so hard. Finally, I resorted to pulling my hair around my face so I could melt into the background more efficiently. This was a wrenching devastation. I honestly thought at least one of my friends would want to send a cupcake to me. While I fought the heartache, I don't think anyone noticed what was happening. I kept my head down as I passed out my valentines. I did not look up when valentines were placed in my mailbox. I didn't even look up when the cupcake cart finally stopped by my desk.

"Lindsey?"

I slowly raised my eyes and nodded. "Here."

One cupcake was placed in front of me. Most of the other kids in my class had four or five, but now my desk was no longer empty. I tucked my hair back behind my ears and picked up the attached note to see who it was from. It said, "A Secret Admirer." The rest was blank.

With that one simple line, all my dreams were restored! A secret admirer! It was so much better than I hoped. My cupcake was a mystery! All of the fools around me KNEW who sent theirs, but mine was the first page of an adventure! My shocked friends crowded around my desk. Even the popular girls came over to see. Who could have sent it? The speculation was delicious. Nobody would admit to it, but why would they? It was a secret! It didn't matter that I only got one. I was the luckiest girl in my class that day.

I lived on that memory for years as my shy, awkward child-hood became a shy, awkward adolescence, and finally turned the corner into a shy, awkward adulthood. If I had a bad day, I would think about my secret admirer and wonder. No matter how badly I felt about a new blunder, I could rely on the memory that some-body secretly sought to make me happy. I had to be worth some-thing. I can't count how many times that sparkling little moment soothed me. I carried it for years.

One day, I happened to be home from college and driv-ing with my sister. Our conversation sparked the memory and I brought up the story. I told her how terribly I was hurt, and how it ended up being so much better than I'd dreamed. I told her how much it helped me feel good, even years afterward. At a stoplight, I happened to glance over at her. She was looking down at her lap with a little smile.

"What?" I asked.

She looked up and said, "It was me."

"What?" I repeated dumbly.

Her smile broadened as she said, "I wanted you to feel spe-cial."

My little sister was two years behind me in school. She knew how much that secret message would mean to me. Then she had the understanding to keep quiet about it, so I could hold on to that feeling all those years. She let me keep the magic. I might have expected to be disappointed when I knew the truth, but I wasn't. I had my mystery for as long as I needed it, and then I found that my admirer had been with me the whole time. It turns out the Laws of Fiction are occasionally correct. For shy, awkward girls, love will often come as a surprise.

Lindsey Monroe-Bougher moved to Chicago to pursue her Bachelor of Fine Arts at Roosevelt University, and spread her awkwardness like the Johnny Appleseed of cringe-worthy silences. Having secured her degree, she retired from the limelight for many years before awakening from dormancy to pen this story.

With the sweet taste of success and an extra-clicky keyboard, she is spurred onward to continue her writing pursuits. Lindsey currently lives in the south suburbs of Chicago with her incredibly supportive husband, a perennially ailing dog, and a cat. All potential descriptors for the cat would be superfluous.

CHAPTER 3: TANDEM THOUGHTS BY ELLEN BLUM BARISH

We were in the Netherlands, so it seemed only fitting that we should rent a tandem bike.

My husband and I were in the country that cycles, celebrating our thirty-fifth wedding anniversary. Renting a tandem had been on his bucket list for a while, but before this trip I'd usually found a way to put the brakes on it.

The streets are too slick.

Visibility's too low.

It's too cold.

Too hot.

Despite the tendonitis in my foot and my claustrophobia in crowds, I gave it the green light because bicycling is David's second love (or so he claims). No matter the occasion or the weather, he will choose the bike over any other mode of transportation.

Let's ride our bikes to the wedding!

You won't even notice the sleet if you're covered in waterproof-breathable outerwear.

I do enjoy a bike ride. But I don't live for it like he does.

However, I knew it would make him happy and I was running out of reasons to resist. Seeing his sky-blue eyes twinkle and his cheeks turn pink is something that I *do* live for. On a bike, he's the embodiment of joy.

He's also a body in motion with a constant proclivity for propulsion. My set point is sitting still. That difference is one of the main tensions between us.

Once on the bike, after assistance from bike shop owners

and a few practice runs, I hadn't anticipated how heavy a double-seated bicycle would be, especially with two grown adults trying to balance on it. I've always liked how easy and fluid biking can be. A subtle lean can initiate a turn. When you get into a rhythm, it can feel like an extension of your body. Not so much when a lefty is the captain and a right-hander is the stoker, and both like being in control. Especially when one of the riders has a bum foot and is navigating urban areas, which leads to stopping at intersections and stabilizing the bike with her foot.

In those first minutes after we left the shop, balanced and upright, I leaned to the right to save my left foot, but he leaned to the left. We were centimeters from toppling, but he swiftly shifted his weight, and with some quick settling steps, we stayed upright.

This ride was going to be harder than I thought.

When David and I started dating in the early 1980s, I liked that he had a lot going on in his life and that he valued self-sufficiency. We were together, but also independent. He was also frenetic, whizzing from class to delivering pizza to a softball game and making it to an evening concert, often in a day. All on his bike.

My main form of exercise was a weekly yoga class, walks at lunch hour, moving my hands around computer keys, and worrying.

I was a worrier. I still am.

Which is what I was doing as we left the city of Haarlem and crisscrossed the streets of Bloemendaal and Zandvoort to the sea. What glorious sights! Only I hadn't counted on not seeing anything in front of me aside from my husband's back. My grip on the handlebars tightened, because even though I trust him, I've seen him drop things. He can be clumsy. But because he navigates city traffic on a regular basis and was wearing his prescription sunglasses, I took a deep breath and tried to let go.

Of the worry. Not the handlebars.

In his work as an attorney, he never walks into a courtroom without a plan. It's the same thing with a bike. He had spent hours, long before we even arrived in the Netherlands, mapping the route.

We were starting to get into a rhythm when we came to a stop by a four-lane highway. David saw an opening for us to get across two lanes to the divider but neglected to tell me. Before I knew it, he was pedaling us into the street. As I hopped on my good foot to keep up, cars were honking at us and drivers were giving us the stink eye until we safely reached the middle.

We'd been canoeing, but unlike that cooperative venture, in which the person at the bow and stern help one another steer, tandem biking was clearly more of a master-slave scenario. My only job was to let him lead.

And I was only going to be good with that for so long.

Once we got beyond the enchanting Dutch residential area and into the country, I began to accept that I would be taking in the sights sideways. I could close my eyes and still move forward as he determined the pace. Like his general demeanor, it was steady. It was just up to me to keep up with it. My pedaling could add or take away power.

So I experimented with this. Because I do that.

"Hey. You're pedaling anxiously. Stay mindful of your cadence, E," he said firmly but calmly, remembering that I respond best when he speaks in a non-accusatory tone.

"What do you mean, anxiously?"

"You are overexpending your energy. You'll tire out. See if you can settle into my pace."

Suddenly he stopped.

"Ack! You need to tell me when you are stopping!"

"Sorry! My shoelace got tangled up."

"We need a safe word. Give me a safe word."

"Stopping. How about 'stopping'?"

"Fine."

The breeze picked up by the sea. The sun shone over spectacular rolling scenery in perfect upper-sixty-degree temperatures. He was happy doing most of the heavy pedaling, and I was good with that. It occurred to me that I hadn't felt this relaxed in a long time. I was actually enjoying this.

Like Chicago, where we live and bike, the Netherlands is flat. But soon a slight incline appeared and threw us off pace.

I called out, "Stopping!" and shimmied off the bike.

I needed a break anyway. I stood for a moment and watched him pedal up the hill. I took in the sea and sand that spanned in front of me and the charming cottages behind.

Over the course of our three-plus decades together, we both have needed breaks. When our daughters were young, I stole writing weekends in Wisconsin and Michigan. He rode the AIDS ride from Minneapolis to Chicago and took week-long bike rides with buddies. We needed that time because there were some seriously derailing years.

Luckily, the topography doesn't stay the same for long.

Our daughters had graduated from college and were now working and living full lives. We had just paid off the final college loan. Our youngest was engaged. I turned sixty. We had not been on a two-week vacation, just us, *ever*!

That's when I planned this trip, which took much discussion and a lot of compromise. We had to select a place where he could ride and that also had art and culture. We had to keep to a budget. Get a good airfare. An affordable Airbnb.

After a scrumptious lunch on the beach, we got back onto our two-seater and David said, "Let's try a different route back."

"Really?"

"Yeah. As long as the sun is at our back, I know we're heading east."

"You're sure? You don't want to look at a map?"

"Nope. I'm good."

This trip had been about making new memories together. All of those rotations had amounted to something.

About half of our married friends are still together. The other half are divorced, widowed, or have chosen the single life. My parents went separate ways just before the thirty-year mark. I know that we are lucky to have found one another. Lots of people love each other, but whatever it is that makes one relationship work longer than another is still a mystery to me.

We were getting close to the rental shop, relying on street signs, when suddenly I had the urge to pick up my feet and position them on the steering stem. Once balanced, I stretched out my arms, like Kate Winslet did when she was secured by Leonardo DiCaprio at the bow of the *Titanic*, and hummed the opening bars of "My Heart Will Go On."

We came close several times, but we never fell over.

Einstein wrote that people are like bicycles. To keep balance, people need to keep moving. But balance also involves the ability to remain still. If you wobble in the seat as the bike is moving, the whole thing can topple over. And if you don't pull over once in a while and take a break, then you will be exhausted.

On the train back to Amsterdam, I closed my eyes and replayed the day in my mind's eye. The ride was not without its bumps or close calls and had taken us across pavement and gravel, flatland and hill, sand and mud, off-road and on. It had been all-terrain. Like our marriage.

Ellen Blum Barish is author of the essay collection *Views from the Home Office Window* and the forthcoming memoir *Seven Springs.* Her essays have been published in *Brevity's Blog, Full Grown People, Literary Mama, Tablet,* and the *Chicago Tribune,* and many of her personal stories have aired on Chicago Public Radio and have been told at Chicago-area storytelling shows. She is editor of the literary publications *Thread* and *Stitch.* Ellen teaches writing at Northwestern University, where she earned a master's degree in journalism, and she also works privately with writers.

CHAPTER 4: ALL KIDS LIE
BY PAMELA MORGAN

All kids lie. I knew that, going into this whole parenting thing. I'd watched thirteen nieces and nephews point fingers, blame siblings, and tell tall tales for over ten years before I had my own. The experts say it's a child's way of learning to navigate the complicated and duplicitous lives that we lead as adults. It is normal. Expected. A natural part of child development. But the first time he lied to me, and I mean, *really* lied, it still took me totally by surprise, shattered all the delusions I had about having this parenting thing down. I'm not talking about an "of course I brushed my teeth and changed my underwear" or an "I didn't color on the wall" level of lie. I'm talking about one of the whoppers.

Kindergarten. Five years old. The Rainbow Chart. For those who have never heard of it, imagine a public display of minute-by-minute behavior. Every day, a child starts on green. Ready to learn. The residue of past spoiled days washed clean each morning at nine. If the child misbehaves, talks out of turn, shouts out an answer, runs, or does any other number of subjectively inappropriate actions, they must cross the room in shame and clip down the rainbow, from green to yellow, yellow to orange, and from orange to the dreaded red, which also includes a phone call home. My child was on yellow a lot. Sometimes orange. The goal, of course, is to move UP the rainbow. From green to purple and from purple to the coveted, elusive, impossible-to-obtain-unless-you-are-Mary-Poppins-practically-perfect PINK. For those of you who know that these are neither the colors nor order of the rainbow, I didn't design the system, I simply exist within it.

I knew pink was impossible. For that matter, I knew purple was a stretch. I didn't expect much. I *wanted* green. Every day, ready to learn. Hands folded and to themselves, mouth closed, eyes shiny and bright with a thirst for knowledge. And I know I dug my own grave on this one, because I admit, I bartered. I figured if I promised the world (or at least ice cream) for getting on purple or pink, I was guaranteed green. And on the very rare occasions that he did make purple, what was a scoop of ice cream to me?

So when, one day well into the year, my child made pink, I celebrated. We had pizza for dinner and ice cream for dessert. I know that you know where this story is going, but believe me, at the time, I didn't see it coming. My honest and truthful little saint, my "no I don't have any homework," "yes I washed all of my body parts" perfect angel could not ... no, WOULD not lie about his behavior at school. And besides, they colored the chart in class ... so naturally I assumed the teacher would know.

When, for the second day in a row, my child made pink, I was through the roof. Then the third day and fourth. I was super-mom. Super Mom with a capital S *and* M. I told my child that if he made a WHOLE WEEK on pink, we would go to Chuck E. Cheese. And not alone! We'd invite all his cousins and friends. The whole neighborhood! And I, of course, would be envied, hailed for being the Greatest Mother On Earth (GMOE)!

I sat on pins and needles all day on Friday. This was our chance to make history. No child had ever made a week on pink, I was certain, and I was the GMOE to artfully and attentively raise said child. When I showed up at school to get him, I didn't even have to ask. The smile that split his face from ear to ear was all the answer I needed. We made pink. We made pink! I danced, right there in the hall of the school, my child laughing and twirling with me. WE MADE PINK!

Down the hall, I could see his teacher. Let's go celebrate with her, I urged him! Let's stand proudly (gloating inwardly) with the most perfect child, which I had created. As I turned to take his hand, my heart sank. Big, fat, guilty tears rolled down his cheeks.

"I lied, Mommy."

It wouldn't register. He lied about today, that's all. Fine, fine, four days is still amazing. Maybe not as epic as five, but still historic.

"No, Mommy, I was never on pink at all. I lied the whole time."

Each word fell like a ton of bricks. Each word popped a bubble that sent me hurtling back to earth. He had lied the whole time. The. Whole. Time.

All kids lie. I knew this. I had lied as a child too. I'd been waiting for it to happen, and yet when it did, it still knocked me right back down to size. As I marched him down the hall to his teacher to confess to this enormous lie, I knew I was confessing my own shame, too. By day two, I should have realized something wasn't quite right. By day three, I should have contacted the teacher to ask. And four and five … those were simply days of pure and unadulterated carelessness. I liked how it felt to have a well-behaved child. I liked how it felt to think that other mothers, who were dragging screaming children or telling their children for the umpteenth time to sit *down* and be *quiet,* for once, *just once*, might envy me. But I didn't have a well-behaved child. I had my child, and he's overactive and loud, wild and antsy. He's prone to dramatics and he's smart as a whip and he really, I mean *really*, loves his ice cream. And it doesn't make me love him any less for exactly who he is.

As I stood there while my child confessed to his teacher, I realized I had lied to myself too. I was terrified of messing up as a mother. I wanted some validation that I was doing something right. I wanted to be on green. And for a single glorious week, I let myself believe that my child's success equaled my success as a parent.

Right now, I was hovering somewhere just above red on the parenting Rainbow Chart. Who did they call for that kind of screw up? I told my son to go wait down the hall when he was done. I stuttered through some apology, offering promises and assurances that I would never let this happen again.

"It's okay. It just goes to show you how very intelligent he is, that he figured out how to get away with it."

Now that she mentioned it, it was smart, wasn't it? Maybe I wasn't Super Mom, but it takes a pretty great mother to raise such an intelligent child!

Pamela Morgan lives and writes in central Illinois with her husband and two children. She has shared stories about parenting with *Listen to Your Mother Chicago*, as well as received a Voices of the Year Honor from BlogHer and second place for Excellence in Blogging from NLGJA: The Association of LGBTQ Journalists.

Pamela prefers being off stage to on and spent two decades working with community theater companies on the south side of Chicago. Her greatest achievement was writing and directing her original play, *A Fairy's Tale*. These days, she spends most of her time raising her family and gathering new material.

CHAPTER 5: ORDEAL AT THE MUSÉE D'ORSAY BY JOHN HAHM

We're in Paris—the glorious City of Light—at the Musée d'Orsay, the cavernous old train station turned into a jewel of a Parisian art museum. Vive la France!

My wife breaks into my reverie. "Here! You take the kids for a while. They're driving me crazy!" She doesn't care to see the Impressionist gallery or *Gauguin as Alchemist* show. She will be in the fashion exhibit right next to it.

So I take charge of my almost-three-year-old daughter Leah and I pat my five-year-old son Josh on the shoulder and I sing out, "Come on, kids! We'll remember this day forever!"

Leah turns around in her stroller and scolds me for not spending quality time with her. "Daddy! Where were you? You don't *appreshunate* us!"

"What do you mean?" I joke with her. "I brought you to Paris, didn't I? What am I then? Chopped liver?"

She pulls out her pacifier and says, "You're ... steamed chopped liver."

"Shut up, Leah," her brother growls, not even looking up from his dinosaur book.

"Josh! Quit fighting with your sister!" I command. "And hey! I'm so glad you're reading!"

Josh replies, "So if I'm not reading, you're not happy?"

It's going to be a long day in the Musée d'Orsay.

On the way to the Postimpressionist exhibit we pass an odd-looking old man in a tan double-breasted suit. He is tall and stooped, with an eye patch. He seems to follow us with his gaze.

But the kids fall into a reverent hush when we enter the sanctum sanctorum of Van Gogh and Gauguin paintings. I lift my little son so he can peer into the backlit display case of Postimpressionist miniatures. The room is dark, and the cleverly illuminated Gauguin paintings are jewel-like in their vibrant colors and exotic forms. "Wowww!" Josh murmurs. "They look like the ladies who sold us leis in Hawaii!"

"Yeah, you're right!" I answer. "These are Tahitian ladies. Find mom, tell her to come over here! She's got to see this." These Gauguin masterpieces are livelier versions of our favorite ones at the Art Institute of Chicago. I let him down and return to those mesmerizingly beautiful paintings.

"Can I see, Daddy?" Leah asks. I stoop to lift her out of her stroller, and then I notice that Josh is gone. I can't see him in that dark crowded room. *Calm down. Think clearly.* It hits me how stupid I was to send my five-year-old son off to find his mom in a crowded gallery at the Musée d'Orsay in Paris. But he can't have gone far. I show Leah the Gauguin paintings. "Ooooh!" she exclaims. I put her back into her stroller. "Hey, I want to look some more!"

I've got to find Josh! He was right here! I can still feel the touch of his hand on mine when I sent him off. He's got to be around here.

"Josh! Hey, Josh! Where are you?" I call out, raising the one banal American voice in a room of elegant French dilettantes and aficionados. I feel their annoyance. But I call out again, "Josh!" After a while, an annoyed French voice answers, "'E eez not 'ere!"

If I could explain that my son is lost, if I could just ask them if they have seen a little boy in navy blue boxer shorts and a black Paris T-shirt. But I don't speak French. I'll bet everyone in that room speaks English and could try to help. But no one does.

I push Leah's stroller out into the jam-packed hallway. There's a kindly looking older woman walking with her granddaughter. I stop her to ask her if she has seen a little boy. "Pardonnez-moi, madame..." But she recoils from me, frowning and shaking her head so hard that the wattles under her chin jiggle. I must look as harried as I feel. I'm half-crying, half-mumbling, "Shit shit shit shit…" as I push Leah's stroller left and right through the indifferent crowds that block my way, dashing through the holes in those crowds. "Shit shit shit shit," I moan.

The crowds move in erratic unison, like schools of sardines. Now and again I think I see Josh in the crowd for just a nanosecond, but then I lose sight of him. I imagine him scared, trying not to cry. But he is not in the swarms of unconcerned humanity who seem to change directions as if by some fishy collective intelligence. Walls seem to separate me from my son. Walls close in on me, cutting me off from any way forward. If I don't find Josh NOW, I cannot live anymore! My mind spirals into chaos. My insides go cold, as I go through futile motions looking for my son. "Shit shit shit shit!" I repeat mindlessly.

My daughter's voice cuts into my paralyzing terror: "Don't say 'shit,' Daddy," she says. "'Shit' is a bad word."

"You're right, Leah," I answer as calmly as I can. It's not her fault that Josh is lost.

"Yeah," she says, turning around in her stroller and looking up at me. Then, in a conciliatory tone, she says, "But you can say, 'Goddamn it…'" I laugh in spite of myself.

Now I'm running with Leah's stroller through the crowds, and bank left and swerve right like Snoopy in an aerial duel with the Red Baron. Through it all, Leah laughs and yells "Whoooah! Yay! Go, Daddy!" as I desperately maneuver through the throngs of people. *Where is he? He was right with me, right here.* Josh was always a fast youngster when running and walking. Even crawling. Is my mind wandering? I've got to focus. But my thoughts are straying now like those sardine-like shoals of humanity. I shout internally at myself: *What do I think this is, some kind of a joke? Wake up! Find Josh!*

But it's no use. I've already run the length of this floor, and there is nowhere else to turn. I'm not religious, but I start to pray.

I feel a calm presence. Not a voice, but a communication. "I'm right here with you. Talk to me."

So I do.

"Please, Lord, he's just a little boy. My life for his."

I feel rather than hear God's reply: "Go now. Find your son. I've given him a message for you."

I feel Leah's small, soft hand on mine. I'll never forget the love and concern in her young eyes. "What's the matter, Daddy?" she asks.

"I don't know where your brother is, Leah."

"Oh, that's all right!" she says.

Was that God's presence I felt? Or Leah's touch? I don't know, but I get up from the bench and start a new search. I do my broken-field run through the crowds, and suddenly I see that tall old man with an eye patch, wearing a double-breasted tan suit, standing in front of me, motioning me to stop. "Your son, lost, monsieur?" he asks. Between his halting English and my worse French, plus a good deal of hand motioning, I understand that he has taken Josh to the Reception and Ticketing office downstairs. I grab his hands and shake them gratefully. "Merci beaucoup, monsieur!"

I pick up Leah's stroller and I'm flying down the staircase at full speed, blasting past a row of sculptures along the white tiled floor, toward the Reception desk. Leah throws her head back gleefully, crying, "Yay! Yay!" and excitedly pumping her fists into the air. There he is in the distance, sitting on the receptionist's desk, calmly reading his dinosaur book. Two beautiful young women are talking to him, and they smile when they see us charging over to them. "'E is very bright!" one of them tells me. I thank her profusely. Leah has stopped cheering and looks grumpy again.

I'm hugging Josh, deeply grateful that he's safe and that I've found him. In a very even tone, Josh asks, "Well, Daddy, did we learn anything today?"

Indeed, I had.

John Hahm recently retired from Northside College Preparatory High School, where he taught English, coached the Academic Decathlon Team, and led educational tours of the UK and EU during spring breaks. He has published a story in *Thread,* a literary journal curated and edited by Ellen Blum Barish, and has presented stories and poetry at Rhino Poetry in Evanston, Soul Stories Live, Fillet of Soul, First Person Live, Pour One Out, This Much is True, and other Chicago storytelling venues.

CHAPTER 6: A PATIENT RAINBOW BY JESSE HALL

They say the definition of insanity is trying the same thing over and over, expecting a different outcome. I've been wondering what happens to this rule when reality reverses it for you—when you do the same thing over and over, with the same result, and then something different pops up. What happens then? Where's reality's clean-up crew?

I got on the right bus and went to the wrong place. This whole ordeal should have been a nonstory. I should have just gone home, but I didn't.

It's the summer of 2006, just before smartphones and portable Google Maps might have changed my fortunes. I'm going into my senior year of college and decide to do an informal study abroad in Ecuador. Out of ten weeks abroad, there are six brief but memorable ones spent volunteering as an English teacher at an elementary school in a farming community in the mountains. Given how short my stay is, I find it difficult to grasp how warm and embracing they are to me. Toward the end of my time there, I get sick, and one night a fellow teacher and his wife sing for me at my bedside, offering comfort as they see my bright flame of enthusiasm reduced to a flicker. It is as beautiful as any music I've ever heard. Steps from where I stay is a beloved greenhouse producing exotic fruit like babacos and taxo that etch new flavors into my memory. From its soil, familiar foods like tomatoes and bell peppers somehow have new succulency massaged into them. Green and rugged mountains lie in the background. At night, one is like a curtain for the moon, drawing back slowly, gently illuminating the long stretch of darkness around me.

Even with everything the community provides, I still venture out to the nearest city about once a week to do things like check my email, buy dry goods, order restaurant food, and simply wander around, maybe running into a fellow traveler. I go by bus and never have any issues. That is, until one afternoon when things turn out differently. I get on the same bus I always do, but this time all the stops are different. Stop after stop, I'm looking out the window and nothing seems remotely familiar. Worst of all, I can't spot the little rainbow. Going out to the community, there's no special sign on the main road letting you know when you get there, so I look out for a little rainbow painted on a small brick wall and take that as my cue to hop off the bus. My eyes are peeled, but it's as if it's hiding from me somehow. Eventually, we get to the end of the route and the bus turns around to head back to the city. Not knowing what else to do, I stay on.

After I get back to the city, I double-check everything that comes to mind: the route, the day of the week, my breath—is it still fresh? It looks like there's one final bus going home today, and without any other obvious options, I'm going to try my chances with it one more time. Predictably, I make the same round trip as before: from the city, to some unfamiliar place, and back again. Now further in defeat, I can feel my confusion and disappointment compounding as it begins to grow dark outside.

Reaching for something that I can't mess up, I consider taking a cab. The word "cab" is a stretch here, as these rides work quite a bit differently than what I am used to. You could call them commissioned community rides—pickup trucks that let you sit in the front while folks hop on and off the back as you continue en route to your destination. Understandably, it is something of a faux pas to hire one, ride out half an hour or so, decide that's not really where you wanted to go, ride back another half an hour, and then forget that you, the one riding in the front with the privilege of air conditioning, don't have any money. Yeah, I have less than a dollar at this point, and he wants fifteen. With my lucky stars now visible in the night sky, we talk; he's willing to accept the groceries I bought earlier that day as payment.

What to do now? On instinct, I walk into the nearest restaurant and dump my problem onto the first poor soul I see standing behind the counter. My expectations are low at this point —I'm just hoping that someone, anyone, can offer me a sliver of advice. This is when I meet a new friend; let's call him Angel. He owns the restaurant, a burger joint, and has a car—two things that make it possible for him to stop the work he is doing immediately and offer me a ride. Very gratefully, I accept.

Go figure—on the first leg of our trip we follow the same route, passing the same stops as I had just done via bus and taxi. Can we revisit the quote on insanity, where you try the same thing over and over? Does it matter that I tried three different modes of transportation, even though I've now made the same trip four separate times? From here we start driving around somewhat aimlessly, making the occasional stop to ask strangers for directions. At one point, Angel pulls the car off the road onto a patch of grass in the middle of nowhere. He then says that we need to get out of the car. I get out. Another car has pulled up alongside us—two doors, no license plates. Several men in plainclothes climb out and Angel mentions that these guys are cops. Figuratively speaking, I pee my pants. A cloud of suspicion and urgency rolls in and I cannot make out a single word of what anyone is saying. Eventually, Angel accepts some commands directed to him and he tells me that we will have to follow them back to the city, with one of their men riding in our car. For a second I'm wondering if I've ever received this much special attention in my life. I get my own chauffeur, complete with a police escort? You would think I was in a parade.

Coming back to Angel's restaurant, I see what looks like his entire extended family standing out front. Some are crying. Angel explains to me what they saw happen, that a strange foreigner had waltzed into his restaurant, had a quick conversation, and then disappeared with him, giving very little notice or details about what they were up to or how long they'd be gone. With several hours passing by, imaginations filled the gaps. Maybe the foreigner had lured Angel into the countryside only to doubly take his car and his life. The police were called, and they certainly did a splendid job tracking us down.

Angel does his best to defuse the situation by explaining the circumstances, but the cops look unimpressed. Questions are flying at me and my odd responses sound silly, even to myself. They are not happy that my only form of ID is the black-and-white copy of my passport I have tucked in my pocket. Following travel-abroad best practices, I keep valuables like my real passport secured elsewhere. Without a word, one of the younger relatives hands me a cheeseburger and soda. Their generosity leaves me in awe—just moments ago, I was a wolf in sheep's clothing, casually walking off a tragic news page and into their lives, ushering their family a devastating loss. Now, with teary eyes drying, they're treating me to their combo special. More importantly, in front of the cops, Angel offers to put me up in a hotel. The unspoken alternative looks to be a night in jail.

Waking up the following morning, thinking I'd be facing the same predicament as before, I'm struck by an idea. Not having any helpful phone numbers on me, I remember that my host organization has a website with a phone number. The little bit of change left in my pocket is enough to go online, jot down the number, and use a payphone. My plan works—I make the call, get directions, and finally uncover the solution to this cosmic paradox that has me trapped inside a parallel universe: there are two places near the city with the same name.

Riding up the main road leading back to the community, Angel at the wheel, we arrive at the brick wall with the little painted rainbow. Ever so patiently, it sits there, waiting to offer a warm hello with all its pretty colors.

◆ ◆ ◆

Drawing from his experiences—time on stage, a professional life wearing many hats, a family of conversational novelists (if that is a thing)—**Jesse Hall** looks to all corners of life for threads of inspiration ready to be woven into the fabric of a story. Jesse lives and works in Chicago, where he recently enrolled in a Newberry seminar on storytelling. As a former student of hers, Jesse would like to thank Jill Howe for her commitment to spreading the joy of storytelling and her passion for the craft. Additionally, he would like to thank all those mentioned in his story—teachers, students, community members (compadres), "Angel" and his family—for their generosity, kindness, and compassion. Finally, Jesse would like to give thanks to Jillian Smith, editor, Linda Hall, mother, Jacquelyn Williams, sister, fellow seminar students, and the folks at the Chicago Story Press for their time spent graciously lending their eyes, ears, and thoughts.

CHAPTER 7: HITTING THE ROAD BY KEVIN BIOLSI

My brother David and I grew up in south central Missouri, but it was an occurrence along a stretch of road in Newport News, Virginia, that provided one of the defining moments in our relationship.

David is three years younger than me, and these days, with both of us now well into middle age, we refer to many of our early interactions as named incidents. For example, the Lincoln Logs Incident occurred when I was ten and he was seven. I had grown tired of him coming into my room uninvited and felt I needed to deter such behavior in the future. After much consideration, having ruled out Hot Wheels, Legos, and an Erector Set as my tools of choice, I took a Lincoln Logs cannister—an old-school Lincoln Logs cannister, mind you, cylindrical and about eighteen inches tall and eight inches in diameter, with a metal lid, and, most pertinent here, a metal bottom—and I half filled it with Lincoln Logs. Only half-full because I'm not a monster. I then balanced it on top of my slightly ajar bedroom door, and with an uncharacteristically welcoming tone, I sweetly called out, "David, can you come into my room?" (I am well aware of the incongruity of trying to discourage him from coming uninvited into my room by implementing a plan in which I invited him into my room. Cut me some slack. I was ten.)

For a brief moment, just before David swung the door open as he entered my bedroom, the sum total of both our happiness levels was off the charts. His happiness level was sky high because I—whom he rightly revered as almost a demigod (or at least that's how I like to remember it)—had summoned him into my traditionally off-limits room. And my happiness level was equally elevated because of the pride I felt in my brilliant plan and the almost giddy anticipation of pulling it off to perfection.

For David, that moment of unbridled happiness was, indeed, very brief. The audible THUNK!, the rattling of Lincoln Logs, and the crying that followed confirmed that my plan had worked like a charm. Looking back, though, I suspect that I may have committed a slight breach of fair play, and I very much doubt that Lincoln himself would have approved of this particular use of his namesake toy.

The Downstairs Hallway Wall Incident came to pass because of a fight David and I had in 1975, when I was eleven and he was eight. Based on the time period, it was probably a heated disagreement about whether Indira Gandhi's state of emergency, which resulted in the suspension of civil liberties and elections, was justified or not. Either that or I called him a poopyhead or something like that. Whatever it was, David jumped on my back, wrapped his arms around my neck, and held on for dear life. In a panic, I quickly determined that, surely, the most effective way to remove him was to back hard into a wall to knock him loose. As it turns out, though, if you forcefully push your younger brother David into a wall, and your younger brother David's point of impact falls between the wall studs, the result is a rather conspicuous younger-brother-David-sized hole in the drywall.

Now, I should note that we were not especially a wall tapestry kind of family, so covering up the hole without raising suspicion was pretty much out of the question. We had to come clean to our parents, who not surprisingly, were unhappy about this gaping hole in their hallway wall. Our dad, a mild-mannered theoretical chemist by profession, proved to be quite skilled at psychological punishment when he employed a very effective means of showing us just how unhappy he was. He repaired the hole by cutting out a nice, neat rectangle in the wall, inserting a like-sized rectangular piece of drywall, taping the seams, and applying and sanding joint compound to make for a nice clean fit. Really excellent craftsmanship. But—and here's the true evil genius of his plan—he didn't paint over this area for years. This incident happened in the hallway that connected David's and my bedrooms to the rest of the house, so we had to pass by that scar on the wall many times, every day, for all those years. I have to give Dad kudos for some pretty top-notch parenting on that one.

With the Lincoln Logs and Downstairs Hallway Wall Incidents as background, I'll move on to the summer of 1977, when I was thirteen and David was ten. We lived in the town of Rolla, Missouri, but we were spending much of the summer of '77 in Newport News, Virginia, where our father was doing some consulting work.

During the day, when Dad was at work, David and I would get around town using the one bicycle that was available to us. There was a wire basket on the back that straddled the rear wheel, with a bin on each side. I would pilot the bike, and David would sit on the basket with one foot in each of the two bins. One of our regular trips was to the Putt-Putt miniature golf course a couple of miles from our apartment, and that's where we were headed when the Infamous Newport News Bicycling Incident occurred.

On these little biking excursions, the main disadvantage for David in our seating arrangement was that he was sitting on unyielding metal rather than a comfortably padded bike seat, so any irregularities in the road were transmitted rather unpleasantly throughout his entire body. And despite the tender portrait of brotherly love that I've been painting for you, it may have been the case that occasionally—or maybe even more than occasionally—I would take advantage of David's seating situation.

So on this particular trip to Putt-Putt, as we traveled along the stony shoulder of the busy road, it's not out of the question that I may have steered toward several significant bumps in our path or especially rough patches in the gravel, all the while ignoring the stream of "Cut it out!s", "Stop it!s" and "I hate you!s" from behind. And as we traversed one notable dip and rise, it's perhaps indisputable that I strategically came up off the bike seat and pulled up on the handlebars to achieve maximum altitude.

When we landed back on solid ground, David's objections

were even more frenzied than before. I looked back over my shoulder. His blaring grievances continued unabated.

But where was David?

I shifted my eyes down slightly. There were his feet, still tucked neatly into their respective bins. The rest of him, however, had been unceremoniously knocked backward and his head was dragging along the unforgiving gravel. And keep in mind that this was the 1970s, before anyone gave much thought to kids' safety, so David's head at that moment was very much a classic '70s-style unhelmeted head.

Even within the context of our storied history, this situation seemed more than a little bit out of bounds, so I applied the brakes and brought us to a screeching halt. I got off the bike and laid it down gently, and as I went to check on the body ... I mean David ... I wondered how I would explain this to Dad. Nothing really came to mind, although I did quickly rule out opening with, "Well, Dad, this is going to put that whole Lincoln Logs thing into perspective."

Based on his struggle to free himself from the bike, the ten-year old's equivalent of a stream of profanity coming from his mouth, and the unadulterated hatred in his eyes, I concluded that David was not, in fact, dead. With as much contrition as my thirteen-year-old self could muster, I helped him disentangle his legs from the bike basket and get to his feet, and I examined the back of his head for any obvious signs of damage.

Ultimately, there were three significant outcomes to the Infamous Newport News Bicycling Incident. First, miraculously, other than having a few minor scrapes, David was physically unhurt. We were soon back on the bike, continuing on our way to miniature golf, maybe just a little more cautiously than before. Second, and perhaps most important, for some inexplicable reason ... that can't be blamed on anyone ... his Putt-Putt game was just a little off that day and I beat him handily. And finally, with that summer of 1977 now long behind us, the memory of that incident clearly still looms large for David: even today, many decades later, whenever we go anywhere together, he refuses to ride on the back of my bicycle.

◆ ◆ ◆

Kevin Biolsi is a statistician by trade but has managed to avoid the glamorous, fast-paced, and ultimately self-destructive lifestyle so often associated with that profession. He also has a doctorate in cognitive psychology that has gone unused for nearly thirty years.

Kevin homeschooled his two daughters for a total of fourteen years, yet even with this clear disadvantage, both have become fully functioning adults. He dabbles in brewing beer, playing the banjo, and gardening. He enjoys running as his sole means of exercise and has served on the board of a youth dance ensemble and a youth theater group while maintaining an impressive inability to dance or act.

Kevin started telling stories in front of audiences in 2016 and found it to be more exhilarating than any drugs he's ever taken, although to be honest, those have almost exclusively been analgesics and anti-inflammatories. One day he hopes to finally tell a story that doesn't revolve around any of his many personality flaws.

Kevin and his wife Carol have lived in Evanston, Illinois, since 1993 and have shared their home at various times with their daughters Lauren and Megan, dogs, cats, rabbits, and a guinea pig.

CHAPTER 8: THE QUANDARY
BY VICTORIA REEVES

I'm all about Ram Dass. Being here now. Speeding down Highway 41 on my motorcycle, I take in the night air. A campfire in the distance, the moist smell of a lawn sprinkler—visceral cues keep me grounded in the ever-evolving present. Despite everything, I realize I am happy. I have what I need: my favorite radio show streaming in my headphones, a future of possibilities laid out before me, and that wonderful feeling of being in flow.

My phone rings. I pull over to answer it.

"Vic, you're coming with me to the appointment tomorrow, right?" my sister says, gasping for breath.

"Sure, Cin, I'll be there. Are you okay right now? Are you in pain?" I'm staring at a huge fir tree and trying to remain calm.

"I'm just afraid," she says. She's crying and coughing uncontrollably.

We've entered into a new world. This is not a person who cries or says they are afraid. This is my big sister Cindy. Bastion of success. Billionaire with a B. Armed with her constantly ringing phone, stunning outfits, gift of gab, and white Tesla, she used her grit to become a real-estate dynamo.

Always in control, she had to win every argument. My dad used to provoke her by saying, "All losers to the back of the bus." Fear of failure fueled her incessant drive.

I remember last Christmas—our grown kids together debating about the state of the nation. A precious moment, but Cindy never sat down. Straightening tablecloths, serving ornate meals on china, she fluttered around making sure everything looked perfect.

She exhausts me. "I'll be there tomorrow, girl. I promise. Just try to rest. Love you." I hang up and pull my Suzuki back out onto the open road.

"Fucking Cindy," I mumble inside the plastic visor of my helmet. "Now I have to be nice to you?"

I'm pissed off. She has not been nice to me. She has condescended, ignored, and minimized me. Like last week, when I drove out to her house. I always take North Avenue west from Chicago, observing the energetic changes. Approaching my sister's fourteen-foot smiling face on a Remax billboard, I know I am close. I begin to feel unmoored.

Cindy, my niece Katy, and I sit in her backyard, surrounded by flowers and a pond with koi swimming lazily back and forth. A gifted gardener, Cindy has made this her sacred space. I'm playing them an archived recording of a storytelling show my husband and I produce.

"I'm so excited about *Soul Stories Live*! People from all over the world are tuning in. I love working with the tellers." I say.

"That's so cool, Aunt Victoria. I know it's helping people understand each other too." Katy smiles.

"Yes, girl. Yes. I'm so glad you get it," I say. She is perceptive, a healer by nature.

My sister, who's been weeding this entire time, grunts, "Good job, Vic." Then she turns to Katy and says, "Don't be like your Aunt Victoria and wait until you're fifty-five to finally be successful."

Did my sister really just use my life path as a cautionary tale?

Wow. Unbelievable and total crap. I've been successful all along. 1. I'm true to myself. 2. My work makes a difference. 3. I've supported my family for twenty years as a creative entrepreneur. Wait. Why am I quantifying my choices?

Moving through space, I pop Jamiroquai into my headphones and try to forget about everything Cindy. I need to restore my peace. I speed up, balancing my 400-pound Suzuki against the pressure of the wind on my chest. When I get home, I walk up the rickety back stairs and open the wood door to the kitchen. My favorite Eleanor Roosevelt quote is on the fridge: "Do the thing you think you cannot do."

"You can do this, Victoria. Detach from drama. Just be present."

I light incense, lie on the wood floors, and meditate.

Centering myself, I try to envision a reality where we can find some common ground, but I can't.

Whatever. We are different. Me with my biracial family and BLM demonstrations. Her with her homogeneous world of straightened hair and gleaming teeth. Oil and water. I am the yin to her yang. I've kept her at arm's length forever, showing up for obligatory gatherings and trying not to go off. She is my only living relative.

This arrangement was working fine until fate drew us together.

After months of weird symptoms that kept getting worse, she has been diagnosed with a rare illness. Me, my sister, and her husband and three daughters sit crammed together in a stuffy exam room at the University of Chicago Hospital. We balance laptops on our legs, take furious notes, and try to understand.

Channeling the drive down on Lake Shore Drive, my hair frizzed out, I stare at my cowboy boots and smile.

The oncologist looks at his chart. "Without aggressive treatment, you have six months to live. You have a rare disease called cardiac amyloidosis."

"Can you spell that, please?" I say.

"Cardiac amyloidosis. Protein deposits are clogging up her heart. Renegade blood cells are replicating in her bone marrow." He educates us.

"So what's the cure?" my brother-in-law Tony asks.

"There is no cure. Only some treatments to perhaps buy more time," he continues.

My God. I try not to freak out. Hit from all sides, my sister is out of breath. She keeps coughing.

He asks about her symptoms. Cindy begins to cry.

"I just get these strange waves of energy all over my body. I don't want to eat. I wake up three to four times a night, covered in sweat." She's holding herself in a ball. "I'm so cold."

"It's okay, Mom," Katy says. "We'll figure this out."

I hand my sister a box of tissues from across the room. I'm sitting on a folding chair, shoved into the corner. Cindy sits on the bed, surrounded by her daughters. At ninety-five pounds, she looks tiny and sad. Her wrinkled sweatshirt has a stain on it. Her hair is pulled back with a scrunchie. I realize I've never seen her with stains or scrunchies.

I want to stroke her hair or comfort her, but we are too far apart.

My feelings are all over the place. How did I get tasked with supporting my nemesis? I've been given medical power of attorney. I will do what needs to be done. I was raised to be there for family.

"So chemotherapy every Tuesday for the next three months. If you stabilize and gain some weight, we may do stem-cell therapy in December," he continues. We are all looking down this dark tunnel, together.

Then it hits me. This is not about me. I can't react to all the toxic things that will be said and done.

Tectonic shifts are happening. My ballbuster of a sister is out of her element. She, the one who kept the Oak Brook Macy's open way past closing time because she was looking for that perfect pair of shoes.

"Yes, Mrs. Banks, no problem, Mrs. Banks, take your time." the saleswoman said, as all the lights around the shoe department shut down and we stood, cloaked in a private cone of service.

Never mind that the saleswoman probably had to get home to relieve her babysitter. Cindy's American Express Centurion Card was like a key to an elite kingdom.

But none of this matters now. There is no status in the cancer ward.

Watching her now, I go through the grief cycle yet again: Denial, Anger, Bargaining, Depression, Acceptance.

I'm grieving for her, and for myself.

Breathe, Victoria, breathe. Have grace. Find that point of humanity.

I know I will be "on call" for doctor's appointments, facilitating hard conversations, and being present for late-night moments of terror.

Be big, Victoria! Get over yourself.

I just want to go home to my husband. I long to lie on our hardwood floors and let acid jazz music wash over me. I want him to hold me.

We all go to the cafeteria to talk over burritos and Starbucks.

My brother-in-law says, "Even though that doctor was Indian, he seemed smart and his English was pretty good."

"Tony! Don't be ignorant," I snap. "He's the head of oncology."

I'm doing one-point meditation, staring at my Om ring.

I'd rather be anywhere but here.

"Well, I grew up in a small town in Wisconsin, so all of this is new for me," he says.

"THIS" is the University of Chicago Hospital system. A virtual hell for somebody like him, where black and brown folks from all over the planet work together with white folks to heal and get healed.

I keep asking myself, "How will I go through this process with these people? How will I be open, kind, generous, and free—with them?"

Our mom died from complications due to MS. We've been down the incurable illness road before. This next chapter will include overwhelming feelings and a need to depend on others, but nuance and powerlessness are not the purview of the uber-successful.

This is a foreign language to them. I will try to escort them into what's next.

My sister is sick, so I try not to judge her. And then—I try—again.

So much trying.

She is picking at her burrito and everyone is begging her to eat.

I read my notes to the group. I suggest we schedule who will drive her and sit with her during chemo.

The duality of this undertaking paralyzes me. I know these people. They will yell and throw their weight around. What a shitshow.

I can see it now. Cindy tethered to an IV, her family wishing they could tip the nurse to get her to move faster. Trying to sell houses to the hospital staff. Giving everyone business cards and smiling like Cheshire cats. Real estate is their family business. It's what they do. It's who they are. Fortunately, they have many connections and are calling in favors left and right. She is getting fast-tracked to see specialists and has the money to cover massive medical bills. It could be worse.

But for her disease there is no cure, only remission. It's a game of time and she has little.

This is NOT how my sister wants to spend her winter. She wants to sit by the pool at her Arizona house, ski in Tahoe, or visit her timeshare in Thailand. She wants to reap the benefits of her hard work. This I understand.

For a brief moment I see how we are both tenacious. We are matriarchs. We are members of a clan of spitfire women who know how to handle adversity. This is our legacy, after all.

My big sister is trying to navigate this terrifying, vulnerable space of not knowing. This may be her biggest challenge yet.

Ironically, this is my strong point: living in the grey area and jumping into the unknown. My quiet power is needed here.

Looking around the table, I see bags under everyone's eyes. For once, nobody is checking their phones.

I put my arm around her. "It's going to be okay, Cin, it's going to be okay."

My role in all of this becomes clear. I will be who I have always been—the one who feels, who listens, who iterates and creates. I will bring beauty into chaos.

I will try to move past our differences and forgive her. Ironically, I may learn how to respect and understand my nemesis. Because then, and only then, will I be able to say goodbye.

Victoria Reeves is a writer, storyteller, and producer, and the host of *Soul Stories Live.* What's her jam? Comedic personal narrative! Victoria loves to channel her parents and other wild characters into her stories. You might have seen her on stage at Story Lab, This Much Is True, Is This a Thing?, The Moth, Inspired Live Lit, Louder Than a Mom, or the Evanston Storytelling Festival. Her one-woman show *BRASSY + INTREPID: Fighting to Be Me* was selected for Lifeline Theatre's 23rd Annual Fillet of Solo Festival in January 2020. Her latest passions include building community one story at a time as the Producer and Host of *Soul Stories Live.* Empowering other women to play and create, Victoria also offers guided exploration in her ongoing virtual course *Creativity Lab - Women Thrive Here.* Curious? Find our more at: https://www.facebook.com/playatcreativitylab

CHAPTER 9: THE VISITATION
BY SHERI REDA

I was no dummy. I knew that fifth grade was entirely shaped and defined by cool, and I knew that cool was beyond my reach. The cool kids just seemed to have something I did not. I couldn't put my finger on it. It was just, sort-of–everything. Here at St. Peters, for example, we all wore uniforms, clean and pressed. I was as clean and pressed as the rest of them. But my shirts weren't crisp, like Marilyn Blaising's. My plaid jumper was loose. My socks fell down when I walked.

I wasn't allowed to watch *Mannix* or *Petticoat Junction*. I was afraid of going upside down during gymnastics class. And my wit wasn't sharp and wounding, like Colleen's. I had the same hair-style as the popular Linda Quagliata, and I put gel and scotch tape on my bangs to keep them straight, but somehow, they always curled on the bus ride into school. And that bus ride! Even if I managed to learn how to dress, talk, and walk like the cool kids, I'd never be cool, because I rode the bus.

At St. Peter's Catholic School, the coolest thing you could be was a walker. Walkers were kids who lived on North Street or Cherry or Walnut Street in Itasca. They walked to school and back, and they had permission to leave school grounds and go home for lunch. Except they didn't go home. They walked up-town and bought candy and hung out with Creepy Cosmo in his comic bookstore in the alley. Walkers were *soooo* cool!

I lived too far from school to be a walker. Every morning of fifth grade, I humped over to Gallagher's corner and huddled with the other outcasts. We straggled in just before it was time for daily mass, too late to take part in the walkers' card and candy trades. Sighing, I plopped down at my desk every day and read the posters that ran like a hanging rope around the top of the classroom: *Honesty is the best policy,* by Ben Franklin. *Industry need not wish,* by Ben Franklin. *Popularity has many snares and no real benefits*, by William Penn.

Wait: *Popularity has many snares and no real benefits?!* That last one drove me nuts because I didn't see any snares. I couldn't see atoms or God or germs either, and I guessed they were there. But the benefits of popularity were as plain as my face. Didn't Sr. Maristella *always* pick Linda Quagliata, who was the gymnastics queen, or Marilyn Blaising, whose nickname was "the blonde bombshell," or someone else like that to crown the Virgin Mary?

Wasn't Colleen Murphy mobbed every time she came back from Cosmos? I knew for a fact that she was; I was one of the mobbers. And what about the four Mary Anns, who went everywhere together, like a built-in party—a kind of porta-party?

I sat at my desk, steaming. *Who did this William Penn think he was? Come to think of it—wasn't William Penn, like, the original "friend"? Like in the Society of Friends?* I wondered what he was trying to pull.

But then I corrected myself. That couldn't be right. Sister Andrea had put those quotes on the board, and Sister Andrea was wise and holy. Maybe I needed to think more deeply. Eventually, I decided that William Penn was like Jesus. He spoke in parables and warnings, and his was fairy-tale advice: *Seek popularity if you dare.*

I didn't dare. Instead, as the school year wore on, I withdrew from the pressure cooker that was social engagement. I sidestepped my mom's nagging to "ask someone over!" I spent most of my time reading, and because our tiny school had almost nothing but saint books, I slowly became radicalized, until I wanted nothing more than to be a martyr. This was something I could dare.

I could be like Saint Eustathius, who was martyred for refusing to eat meat on Fridays. He became incorruptible, his flesh still intact even to this day. I would love it if I never decayed! Unfortunately, my mom insisted I eat everything on my plate.

I turned to Father Damien of Molokai. He went to help the lepers in Hawaii, and he lived with them happily for twenty years before he became a leper, too, and won his place in heaven. That could be my long-term goal, but I wanted something I could do now.

I didn't think I could get anyone to stone me, like they did Saint Stephen. And no one would punish me as they punished St Agnes, for refusing to give up her virginity. Anyway, no one was asking. And anyway, I wasn't quite sure what that experience was like.

But then I found the Cinderella of Catholicism: Bernadette! She was young and beautiful, but she mostly went unnoticed. She prayed a lot, and Mary appeared to her and told her to build a shrine just like the one I had already built for the boy I liked! Bernadette wasn't *killed* for her beliefs, but she did suffer. Her suffering was the poignant pain of having something to say—and never being heard.

That could be me! I knew just the spot where Mary could appear to me. There was a clearing in the little woods on the edge of the playground where no one ever went, where balls got caught in the thorn bushes.

It would be perfect. I would just go there every day at lunchtime recess until my devotion became evident, and then, one day when everyone had faded from my prayerful mind, Mary would appear to me, and only me. She would tell me things—important things that the Pope would have to keep secret until the year 2525. And I would go on TV and plead with him and all Catholics everywhere to believe me. And people would pray to me and get cured. This plan would work! Finally, I had a purpose in life, a reason for being! And, well, a backdoor entrance into popularity.

I went there month after month after month after month. Nothing.

I knelt on dry, poky leaves and ice and snow. Nothing.

May—Mary's Month—came and went. I had suffered at the edge of every end-of-recess crowning, to no avail. I had prayed the prayers I knew ceaselessly, and I began to give up on my destiny.

One day right before school let out, I had an especially discouraging day. It was too rainy to visit the clearing in the woods during recess. And then I had dropped my homework papers on the wet floor of the bus. And when I got home that afternoon, I found that my little brother had scribbled all over my Bobby Sherman poster.

My mom was having a girls' night out, but she said I couldn't come—I didn't count. I had nothing to do that night but relive that day's particular humiliation: I'd told Jim Perry I liked him, and he said: "Well, don't."

I was so discouraged that I went to bed *before* my nine o'clock bedtime. But almost as soon as my head hit the pillow, I found myself transported to a glass enclosure filled with light. There was a big, spiral marble staircase there—like the one with Georgia O'Keefe's *Clouds,* at the Art Institute—except it had a landing. And on the landing—there she was.

Mary.

She seemed to be made of marble, like the staircase. But then she moved, and she smiled at me! And then something horrible began to happen. Mary took off her blue mantle and left it crumpled beside her on the marble floor. And her feet—her bare feet were not holding down that snake. *Where was the snake?*

I looked around, overcome with anxiety. When I turned back to the Virgin, the anxiety blossomed into full-blown panic. Mary had begun to unfasten her girdle—that sash she wore around her waist. She let it fall to the floor, on top of the mantle. Her tunic fell free. Mary rolled her shoulders and bent her knees, one at a time, freeing her hips to sway.

It came to my horrified dream-self that Mary was undressing! She was taking off her tunic, and I was a witness.

I couldn't stop this dream. I was frozen to the spot. Besides, I wouldn't have the temerity to touch the Blessed Virgin Mary. It didn't occur to me to shout out, but I am sure that my shout would have been strangled. All I could think in my shock was that *I had to get out of there.*

So I gathered up all the determination I'd been born with,

all the strength I'd amassed from withstanding my isolation, all the concentration I'd built up through prayer, and I reached into my consciousness and shook it hard. I invaded my dream life and —

I. WOKE. MYSELF. UP.

I sat up in bed like a straight-backed chair. Slowly I regulated my breathing, although my heart kept pounding in the dark. I was so relieved to be safe. Solitary. Ignored, even. I could make my peace with being uncool and ignored. I had had my visitation, and my world had changed forever. But I was pretty sure I couldn't tell the Pope—or anyone else—about this.

Sheri Reda is a writer, editor, and performer whose three Master's degrees—in Modern Letters, Religions and the Arts, and Information Sciences—support her work as a communications consultant, writer, and performer. She is also a certified Master Life-Cycle Celebrant whose personalized weddings, memorials, and other ceremonies have been rated among the best in the United States.

Sheri's writing has been published in *Thread*, *The Examined Life*, and other journals and has been anthologized in *The Healer's Burden*, published by the University of Iowa Press. Her plays are included in *The Infinite Wrench*, by Chicago's Neo-Futurists. Her chapbook of poems, *Stubborn*, is available through lulu.com. When she's not hiding from COVID, Sheri tells adult stories throughout Chicago and presents children's stories at Wilmette Public Library.

CHAPTER 10: PAPA AMERICAN
BY LYNNE JORDAN

My grandfather was the son of a female slave and the white man who owned her. He was one of fourteen children born in the state of Georgia in 1883. "Papa," as we called him, was the patriarch of my family. Papa was a big, handsome, strapping man with a voice that rumbled like thunder when he preached or when he was angry. And sometimes, he was very angry. Papa had no formal education, yet when he eventually fled the South for Dayton, Ohio, he was able to find work. He was the first black man hired by the city of Dayton to be a garbage man. At that time, the city hiring a black man for any position was momentous. Later, he sent for his family and started a church called St. Luke Missionary Baptist, which is still standing and going strong today. Papa had nine children. My mother, Maude, was the youngest. I grew up in Papa's church, which is where I learned to sing.

When younger family members would see a picture of him, they would ask: "Who is that white man?" When they learned THAT was Papa, they were stunned. They knew him only as an old, bald, stern patriarch. They had no idea he was so imposing and attractive. Later in life, when he would have his picture taken, he was never seated. He would always stand tall, wearing tails. That was Papa.

He died when I was seven years old. But I still remember him well. As a little girl, I heard the stories of his standing up to the White Man, or to any man who disrespected him. Papa didn't take no mess, which means ... I loved the stories of his childhood. When he was a child, he used to preach to the folks working in the fields. Someone would hoist him up on a tree stump or a box in the cotton fields, and he would let go with a sermon to all the field hands while they worked in the hot sun. There he stood, this prodigy full of fire and brimstone. The workers would smile and give witness—"Amen!" "Preach, Dave, Preach!"—as this man-child recited scripture from the Bible, scripture he had memorized. It must have been an amazing sight. Everyone knew he was special, anointed—the "Golden Boy." Later in life, his children thought he was a tough, hard man, and his grandchildren thought he was mean. They were all afraid of Papa. Except for me, the youngest. The last child of his youngest child.

But it was a miracle I ever knew him.

Papa's life was a journey. At times, a very dark and scary journey. In the early 1900s, Papa had married and begun having children. Papa and his family lived with his mother, Grandma Fannie, on a little farm in Georgia. The neighboring farm was owned by a white family. Surprisingly, back then, some blacks and whites lived in the country as neighbors—so to speak—share-croppers trying to eke out an existence in poverty. Papa may have even considered the neighboring farmer a friend. Their kids may have played together in the fields. Often these men, these young fathers, borrowed tools from one another to plow their fields, as neighbors do.

But one day, they got into a disagreement over one of the tools. It wasn't a big brawl. But it came to blows when the neighbor called Papa a "nigger." Typical. White folks used to refer to African Americans as "niggers" every day. HA! They still do. But to Papa, that ugly word triggered a natural response. Papa hit him right in the mouth. And that was the end of the fight. Both men returned to their fields. Later that night, Papa told his mother, Grandma Fannie, about the little scuffle in the fields. He spoke with an aura of pride. Papa showed that cracker he would not be disrespected. But Grandma Fannie wasn't proud. She was horrified. "SON, DON'CHA SEE WHAT YOU DONE?! THEY GON' KILL YOU!"

At the farm next door, the neighbor was telling his own story. No black man hits a white man—neighbor or not, friend or not. On the street, a black man can't even look at a white man in the eye. You have to speak with respect: "Yes, suh. No, suh." And you certainly didn't punch a white man for calling you a nigger. No way. Never. So the neighbor puts on his cloak of entitlement as he tells the story to his friends. And the crowd is fired up: "Let's go get him!" "We'll teach that nigger a lesson." "Yea!" "YEAH!" "WHOO!"

That's how it was done. The lynch mob would gather the good ol' boys. They would get their guns and some torches, and set out into the night. They would go to the house, stand outside with their burning torches, and drag him out, while his wife screamed and his children sobbed. They would beat him, set the house ablaze, and maybe the fields too. Then they would drag him away to the lynch site—usually an old tree—put a rope around his neck, hang him, then set him on fire. Maybe even take some pictures to show.

> Southern trees bear a strange fruit, *
> Blood on the leaves and blood at the root,
> Black bodies swinging in the southern breeze.
> Strange fruit hanging from the poplar trees.

That was the fate Grandma Fannie knew her son would face. Unless she could find some way to stop it. She went to the white man she worked for, seeking his help. But all he did was tell her to get her boy out of town. Now.

Grandma Fannie was a resourceful woman. Her greatest personal accomplishment was always that she kept her family—all her surviving children—together throughout that entire ordeal that was Slavery. She watched other children ripped away from their mother's breast, but not her children. She kept them alive and by her side. God willing, her son would not die that night.

In the darkness, she sneaked her beloved David away from his home, from his wife and young children. She took Papa deep into the woods and hid him in a fallen, hollowed-out tree log. There, encased and hidden away, Papa disappeared from the face of the earth. Days went by, a week, and there he stayed until she could get money to send him away to the north, to safety.

I have lain awake many nights, imagining the horror he must have endured. The fear for his wife and young children, the anguish of being ripped from them, all too aware they might never see each other again. Listening to the sounds of the forest, the insects gnawing into his flesh, the smells, the claustrophobia. The terror of lying there, night after night, fearing the savagery that awaited him if he were discovered.

"COME OUT HERE, NIGGER!"

Every night, Grandma Fannie sneaked out to the hollow log. Quietly, in the darkness, filled with the fear of being seen and followed, she took him food to keep him alive. By the light of the Georgia moon, she delivered sustenance and love.

Grandma Fannie had three sons who had already fled the South and gone North. Somehow she got word to them to send money, so their brother could escape. The message went to Clifford in New York, Fred in Philadelphia, and John Henry in Ohio. The money from John Henry came first. And that's why Papa moved to Ohio. And that is how, in 1961, I came to be born in Dayton, Ohio, the youngest grandchild of David Revere, "Papa."

My grandfather was headed to a lynch man's rope. But thanks to the dedication and determination of his glorious mother and the grace of God, a miracle happened. David Revere did not die. He lived. Unlike so many others.

> *Southern trees bear a strange fruit,*
> *Blood on the leaves and blood at the root,*
> *Black bodies swinging in the southern breeze,*
> *Strange fruit hanging from the poplar trees.*
>
> *Pastoral scene of the gallant south,*
> *The bulging eyes and the twisted mouth,*
> *Scent of magnolias, sweet and fresh,*
> *Then the sudden smell of burning flesh.*

> *Here is fruit for the crows to pluck,*
> *For the rain to gather, for the wind to suck,*
> *For the sun to rot, for the trees to drop,*
> *Here is a strange and bitter crop.*

*"Strange Fruit," recorded by Billie Holiday in 1939, written by Abel Meeropol and published in 1937.

In a city brimming with classic blues and jazz voices, **Lynne Jordan**'s voice stands out as a vocalist, bandleader, solo performer, and storyteller. Drawing upon her own personal stories gleaned from fifty-eight years of living, her experiences are always poignant, often funny, and always accompanied by a song.

Born in Dayton, Ohio, in a loving blue-collar home, she was sent to all-white schools (imagine the wealth of material there) and Northwestern University, where she began crafting her voice for singing, acting, and storytelling. Time went on and Jordan created a bank of stories about her struggles with weight, show business, aging, arthritis, and race, as well as ancestral stories: Jordan's great-grandmother was born a slave and her grandfather was a revered preacher and entrepreneur who escaped a lynch mob under the clever protection of his mother.

Jordan has performed her works at numerous live lit shows in Chicago, New York, Atlanta, Moscow, and Paris. Because she is a popular entertainer in Chicago, she has honed her storytelling skills with every song, in every concert and event, and in a solo show with music called *A Great Big Diva.*

CHAPTER 11: THE BALLET CLASS BY STEPHANIE ROGERS

It's the middle of the winter and I've squeezed myself into a leotard and tights like a six-week camping trip packed into an overnight bag. My ankles are the same circumference as the thighs of everyone else in the room.

I am here because I'm desperate for joy, but I've been wrongly assigned to this class. When I called to inquire about ballet for adults, the studio manager asked if I had any previous dance experience and instead of confessing that I was a pasta lover who hadn't danced in decades, I rattled off an inarguable resumé.

"Well, I was in a *modern dance troupe* in college...and took *years* of ballet...and once studied advanced hip hop..."

All of the rock bands and orchestras I've sung with since college have taken a massive toll on my ears and I have a case of tinnitus so severe that I cannot sleep, read, drive, or think. Healers, doctors, diets, sound programs, meditation classes, and admonishments to God have produced no results and I am a diminished version of my former self.

So, I've come to the ballet barre.

I loved ballet when I was a kid. There was nothing like the exhilaration of running up the creaky staircase to the second floor of the Gus Giordano Dance Center on a busy Saturday morning to inhale the sweet, thick odor of ballerina sweat and worn toe shoes! Ballet was edgy, exciting.

Yet being an outsider here in class, in this world where I once belonged, is beginning to cause tremendous angst. I am the oldest person in the room by at least thirty years and the fattest by more than forty pounds.

My God, the nubile derrières!

My classmates are eight professional dancers and two homeschooled prodigies who spend all day at the studio. There's an arrogant ballerina warming up next to me with freakishly long legs and on the other side of Snooty Long Legs is what appears to be my friend Eleanor's seventeen-year-old daughter Lily Swedlow.

"Hi Mrs. Rogers," sings Lily. "What are you doing here?"

Fuck you, Lily. I'm wondering the same thing myself! All I know is that I struggle to sleep because the ringing in my head is unbearably loud and I'm here to find just one lousy moment of joy and peace! By the way, it may not look like it now, but I used to be adorable, Lily!

That is not what I say.

I say, "Lilyyyyyy! How's the homeschooling going?"

But I'm worried.

The manager on the phone told me the music in class wouldn't be very loud, but with overly sensitive ears, you just can't trust anyone else's definition of loud. Music has hurt me before. Just weeks ago, I was in the back row of a concert hall listening to a quiet folk trio and my ears were in agony (not because it was *folk* music).

Turns out, the delicate piano sounds are quite soothing. It's the dancers who are not. Despite my limited experience, I know that dancers hate whomever sucks the most. Also, dancers hate whomever is the best. Dancers are haters. I had forgotten this.

Lily just ignores me, but everyone else redirects all of their self-loathing and body dysmorphia onto their disgust for the old fat lady, and Snooty Long Legs is the premier hater of them all. She glares at my hips, confirming her profound disgust for *Le Dance Disaster* I've become.

I had to quit my dream job of leading an event band and there have been a few moments where I've wondered if I could continue to live with this incessant noise.

So I've gotten myself to ballet class, albeit by falsifying my physical status and exaggerating any aptitude.

I move to the back of the room and I carve out my own little fat lady row. The tall ballerinas are like elegant redwoods blocking me in the mirrors, so thankfully neither they nor I can see the unbridled spectacle I've developed in the back.

I'm having a ball! My ears, body, and disgrace are elatedly at ease.

Unfortunately, after thirty minutes of free-form bliss, I hear the instructor demanding that we line up in pairs. We'll now perform the steps we just learned for the entire group.

Fuck.

The closest person to me—and most displeased, of course— is Snooty Long Legs. We both know that one of us will soar with the grace of a thousand gazelles and one of us will look like a bouncing piece of sausage.

Maybe I should take a bathroom break. Or hear my phone ring. Or hobble my way to the chairs just outside the room.

Just pulled a muscle! Sorry, can't dance!

I'm a middle-aged woman. I do not have to tolerate the humiliation of dancing in front of a room full of professional dancers. Yet somehow, I take my place right next to Snooty Long Legs and I am boldly invigorated. I will not be robbed of joy!

It's game on, ballerinas.

The music begins and the instructor counts us off. One, two, three...two, two, three.

And I dance. I dance my heart out! Not the combination we were to have learned, obviously, but a distinct choreography of my own creation.

I dance for anyone who has ever felt old or fat.

I dance for plights unseen. For the disappearance of grace.

I dance for anyone who's been made to feel unworthy in a room.

I spring toward the door and produce one final farewell flourish, bidding Snooty and the gang adieu.

I got what I came for.

Joy.

❖ ❖ ❖

Stephanie Rogers is the creative director of Story Jam, a live music and storytelling show/podcast in which true, personal stories are coupled with original songs. Steph holds a B.A. in Theatre from Northwestern University and an M.A. in Written Communication from National Louis University. She leads storytelling classes, workshops, and retreats through Story Jam Studio.

www.hipchick.com
www.storyjamshow.com
www.storyjamstudio.com

CHAPTER 12: THE ONE WITH THE CHATROOM BY ERICKA MCFEE

Ah, the '90s! It's a decade that can be remembered for so many things. All those movies. Those songs. That fashion.

Okay, maybe not so much the fashion. Although you have to admit, flannel shirts were pretty comfy and versatile.

What I remember the most about the '90s is that it was the Dawning of the Age of the Internet. Of course, the internet didn't have nearly the amount of content back then that it has now, but it still had the potential for being a huge time suck.

The place where people seemed to spend the most time online was the internet chatroom. I hold one of my friends from high school responsible for introducing me to the world of chatrooms, where people didn't go by their actual names, but rather "NSyncFan42" or "HoosierDaddy69."

I was visiting my friend at her house when she was exchanging messages with people in these chatrooms, particularly with her "boyfriend."

At least someone she *thought* was her boyfriend. Someone she *thought* was a guy.

Those of us from small towns understood "catfish" to be a noun, specifically a thing you ate, preferably breaded and fried. To us, "catfish" wasn't a verb. It wasn't something we thought people actually *did* to each other.

I found this chatroom phenomenon weird but also fascinating. You could communicate with people from all over the country, even the world. It seemed like the perfect place to escape the real world. The *actual* real world, not the MTV show.

It was also the perfect social outlet for a young person like me, who spent so many years being tragically unpopular. Practically clueless. Having grown up in a small town without much exposure to this brave new digital world, I headed off to Indiana University. I was a small fish in a big pond. A pond made infinitely bigger with unfettered internet access.

I don't even know why I was taking out loans to pay for a dorm room when I practically lived in the campus computer lab. I squandered much of my early college career there, putting off writing my term papers, conversing with people in these chatrooms instead. I could have socialized with any number of my 30,000-plus classmates. But the *online* friends I was making in these chatrooms just seemed to *get* me.

Especially this one guy. He lived in a suburb in western Pennsylvania. Allegedly.

He was a little older, late twenties. Allegedly.

He had recently finished his MBA and was in search of a job while he was helping out his parents and grandparents. Allegedly.

We bonded over our shared passion for musical theater. I had been a band and drama geek in high school. He had been in show choir. As for what he looked like, I had no idea. Smartphones didn't exist then. Even if you had a physical photograph of yourself, you needed to scan the photo and upload the file to a floppy disk, etc. And what kind of weirdo walked around with a bunch of pictures of themselves?

I took his description of his appearance at face value, so to speak. The image I had in my mind was good enough for me. I was smitten.

We had been talking for a couple of months—or maybe it was just a few weeks, which seems like months when you're young. Before long, the subject of meeting "IRL" came up. For those of you who aren't hip to the lingo, that means "in real life." What weekend would we finally meet? Who would do the traveling? As someone who hardly ever went anywhere, I volunteered to fly out to meet him. But I needed a way to get there.

Dad5523 has just entered the chatroom.

One day, when talking to my dad on the phone, he asked me about the social scene at IU. I had attended a couple parties at that point. But otherwise, I honestly had no idea what the social scene was like, because I spent most of my free time and then some in the chatrooms. I decided it was time to break the news about "the guy."

"Oh great!" he said. "Well, just remember to use protection."

"Oh, that won't be necessary," I replied.

There was a long pause. "What do you mean, 'It won't be necessary?'"

Nervous laughter. "Oh, that's because we haven't actually met in person yet."

"You haven't *met* him yet? What do you mean that you haven't met him yet? You just said he was your boyfriend!"

I explained to him, best as I could, about the chatrooms and how we met. I also mentioned that I was, in fact, planning to meet him soon, but I needed to find a way to get there. My dad didn't think that meeting this guy was such a terrible idea. After all, he's from that bygone era where people actually met their paramours "IRL" because "real life" was the only kind of "RL" there was.

My dad offered to fly me out there. And by fly, I mean actually fly me there. You see, he was a pilot. He didn't fly for a commercial airline, but he did have a pilot's license. Better yet, he had his own little plane.

So we made plans to fly, my dad and I, out to western Pennsylvania so I could meet this guy. Alas. It all came crashing down.

The *plans*, I mean. The plans came crashing down. Not the plane!

My dad had the type of license that prohibited him from flying if the visibility was poor. And it *was* poor. After my classes were done on Friday, the only thing that was clear was that we would be in for some terrible storms that were expected to last the whole weekend.

I wasn't just disappointed. I was impatient. And stubborn. And determined. My dad tried to convince me to wait for a different weekend when the weather would be clear. But—*no*. I had to go *that* weekend. How could he not understand that? He was young once, right? He had been in love once, right?

I managed to convince one of my "IRL" friends at IU to give me a lift to the airport in the middle of the night so I could take the first available red-eye flight to rendezvous with my Romeo. My friend didn't even bother trying to talk me out of going. Maybe he figured that once I finally got there and saw just what a creep and weirdo this guy was, I would finally shut the hell up about him.

I had a pleasant and uneventful flight to Pennsylvania, except that I landed at the airport nearly an hour later than the scheduled arrival time. What if he had been waiting for me, and thought I stood him up, and he went home? I would be stuck at the airport all weekend. I wouldn't get to meet him. Even worse, he would vanish into thin air and I would never hear from him again!

Yes, these were my concerns. That we would have a missed connection or that he would be upset with me. I was oblivious to the possibility that I could have been pushed into the back of an unmarked windowless van, whisked away to who knows where.

I got off the plane and practically sprinted to baggage claim. Not that I had to worry about any suitcases. I just brought my duffle bag. But I thought and hoped that he would still be waiting for me there.

When I got down to the baggage claim area, I saw a young man standing near one of the carousels, slightly turned away from me, frowning at his watch. He matched the description I had been given. OMG. Was it him?!

I went over to this strangely familiar man and tapped him on the shoulder. He turned and looked at me. And gave me a big smile. He knew. I knew. There was no doubt.

I have no idea how long we stood there in a passionate embrace. It seemed like forever. It felt like reuniting with a loved one whom you hadn't seen in years. But we had never seen each other before that day. As it turns out, he was *outrageously* good-looking.

On a scale of Johnny Depp to Brad Pitt, he was a Luke Perry.

We got into his car and headed to his house. Technically, it was his parents' house. But his parents were out of town that weekend. *How convenient.*

On the way to the house, we shamelessly sang along to cheesy '70s love songs that played on the radio. As we serenaded each other with songs like "You Are the Woman" and "We've Only Just Begun," I felt like I was perched on the bow of the RMS *Titanic*, as though I were flying. Life couldn't possibly get any better than it was in that moment. But the best was yet to come, as it were.

We got to the house. I set my duffle bag down. And then IT. WAS. ON. Hormones and pheromones, people. Powerful stuff. Let me tell you, it was so nice being in a real house instead of campus housing, and on a real bed instead of a dorm room bunkbed with a roommate unsuccessfully pretending to be asleep nearby.

And yes, we *did* do things that weekend that required wearing clothes and actually leaving the house. Like visiting his grandmother, whom he admired more than anyone else in the world. I felt honored that he introduced me so quickly to someone who meant so much to him. That had to be a good sign, right?

To say I had a wonderful weekend would be an understatement. There were certain aspects of that weekend, and my relationship with the guy, that I vividly remember. Even after all this time.

Except for his name. *That* detail, for some reason, I don't remember. It could have been Mulva, for all I know. But when it finally came time to say our emotional goodbyes at the airport, he gave me a huge hug, a long kiss, and a beautiful rose as I boarded the plane back to Indiana.

As soon as I got back to my dorm room, I put the rose in some water—in a red Solo cup—and sat the cup on my windowsill. Much like our online relationship, I tried to keep it alive as long as I could. But like the rose, the relationship eventually died. Apparently, our love wasn't meant to be IRL.

◆ ◆ ◆

Ericka McFee is a Chicago immigration attorney who has spent years telling the harrowing stories of her clients who have fled persecution in despotic countries around the world, seeking safety in the United States. Drawing upon her own life experiences—much less harrowing, but often crazy and challenging—she recently began her personal storytelling journey.

Ericka enjoys studying languages. She speaks German, Italian, Spanish, and French, with varying degrees of fluency. From her martial arts training in college, she can also speak some Korean and Japanese. She earned a Bachelor of Arts in Germanic Studies from Indiana University and a Juris Doctor from New England Law | Boston.

Ericka is also an avid hockey fan. When she is not busy running a law practice, she is either watching or playing hockey year-round. She lives with her husband Neal and their two dogs, Layla and Buster, in the western suburbs of Chicago.

CHAPTER 13: HITCHHIKING MOUNTAIN ROADS BY MARGARET BURK

Robin and I stood on the side of the road: bell-bottom jeans (mine purple, hers red), tie-dyed T-shirts, long hair (mine straight, hers wild), our thumbs in the air.

We were in our mid-twenties and hitchhiking from Chicago to LA.

Robin growled at a passing car, "Who are these people? How can they see two girls standing on the side of the road and not stop?"

She pulled her thumb in and handed me the cardboard sign that said "Salida" (which was the next town down the road), sat down, opened the food pack, and started eating again.

Should we have stayed on the main highway in Colorado, with steady rides? It was that last billboard of the Marlboro Man that inspired us to choose the state roads through the mountains in hopes of meeting a real Marlboro man.

Robin dumped a fistful of trail mix in her mouth and mumbled, "I think a Marlboro Man would be named Bruce."

"Bruce? No."

"Jesse, like Jesse James," she continued.

"No," I responded, "Hank. Hank. That's it."

It was mid-July, with a big open Colorado sky and billowy white clouds. We inhaled that clean, fresh mountain air for another hour and another hour as vehicle after vehicle passed us by.

The sun disappeared. I looked up. A huge dark rain cloud. *What? Storms don't just show up instantaneously.* In the Midwest they develop. This one was developing—fast. The sky opened.

We pulled yellow plastic rain ponchos out of our back-packs and slid them on. Robin threw back her head and splayed her arms, exclaiming, "Zeus, great god of sky and thunder, come to the aid of these fair damsels in distress!"

We were theatre people.

Zeus responded by sending us rescue. Headlights were coming up the road. We waved our thumbs frantically.

The headlights slowed. A small old blue Chevy pickup truck passed, then pulled to the side of the road and stopped. We grabbed our packs and ran.

I have to explain. It was 1972. Young men and women were hitchhiking all over the country. Inspired by author Jack Kerouac and musician Woody Guthrie, we wanted to see the country and meet the people. There were so many of us sometimes, we would stand in line to get a ride—sharing food and stories with other hikers.

Long haul truck drivers were the kings of hospitality. Young people too, radios blaring—Jimi Hendrix, Johnny Cash, Bob Dylan. It seemed we knew each other by our music.

The passenger window of the pickup truck rolled down. A man with thin sandy hair shouted, "Are you girls okay?"

"Trying to get to Salida. We'll find a motel there."

"You hitchhiking?"

"Yes."

"I'm not going as far as Salida. But you don't want to be out in this rain."

The whishing of the windshield wipers filled a long pause.

"I could put you up with me and my family for the night. It's a bit of a way up the mountain. I'll bring you back down to the road in the morning."

I sized up the situation quickly. I didn't smell alcohol or marijuana. He seemed sincerely concerned. I heard my sister's words, "You're going to die on the road." Rain beat loudly on my poncho. We were at 7,000 feet above sea level, night coming, the chance of another ride slim.

"Yes!" I said and looked at Robin. Her mouth opened. I made

a quick gesture for her to shut it.

He jumped out, picked up our backpacks, and threw them under a tarp in the truck bed as we climbed into the cab—me in the middle, Robin by the window. He slid back behind the wheel.

"My name is Margaret. This is Robin."

"Nice to meet you. Name's Jesse."

Robin and I took a slow double take. Was this our Marlboro man?

Jesse edged slowly back onto the two-lane road. Bluegrass played on his radio.

"Where you girls from?"

"Chicago, we're headed to LA. Never been in the Rockies before."

"This is God's country. Lived here all my life."

The rain eased up as he turned off the highway on to a dirt road that headed up the mountain. Trees lined both sides. The smell of pine was pungent and spicy. Now and again a simple house was nestled in the thick woods.

"Kids will be surprised when they see what I brought home. Wife will have dinner ready."

The rain stopped as he made a quick right turn onto a narrow, bumpy road full of ruts. Robin and I planted our feet and put our hands on the dashboard to brace ourselves as he slipped the truck into low gear, stepped on the gas, and propelled us up a steep hill. Robin gasped and sputtered, "Your sister's right. We're going to die."

Then a clearing appeared with a small wooden tin-roofed house. Four children and two dogs played in the scruffy yard (too much shade there for grass). Jesse parked the truck and jumped out.

"Daddy," the children cried as they ran to him. They stopped when they saw us inside and drew back. The youngest ran inside.

"I got a surprise for y'all," Jesse called as Robin and I got out of the truck.

His wife appeared—a simple woman in a cotton dress with

long brown hair, her face unreadable, children clinging to her skirt.

"Helen, Annie, Jesse Jr., Samantha, and Billy, this is Margaret and Robin. They were hitchhiking on the road in the rain. I said they needed a roof over their head tonight and a home-cooked meal."

After the second long pause of the day, Helen, his wife, said, "Annie, go set another two plates."

Jesse led us inside; there was a main room, fireplace on one end, wooden table in the middle, kitchen on the other end. The aromas of home-cooked food welcomed us. Robin and I sat on the couch taking it all in. Jesse sat on the floor and the kids piled on top of him, taking us in.

Helen called us to the table. We ate biscuits with sausage gravy, fresh tomatoes, and green beans. The conversation flowed. Bite by bite, four-year-old Samantha leaned closer and closer to me until she found the courage to whisper, "I like your shirt."

I held out a corner of my tie-dyed shirt. "It's okay. You can touch it." She beamed.

After dinner Robin and I took the kids to play outside: duck, duck, goose and some theatre games, giving Jesse and Helen some time to themselves on the porch.

Then Robin brought out her ukulele and picked some bluegrass tunes. The children danced. We danced. Jesse and Helen danced.

At nightfall I crawled into my sleeping bag by the fire, grateful for the warmth of the smoldering embers. It did get cold and it did rain. As I listened to the sound of rain on the roof, I thought, *I wish my sister could see us here.*

We were up early, had breakfast, said goodbyes. The children were sad to lose their playmates and waved as Robin and I climbed into the truck. Jesse threw our packs in the back, drove down the mountain, and dropped us off on the road.

"You girls stay safe now," he yelled out the window as he drove away. We waved as we watched his truck disappear in the distance.

In the years since I've often thought about Jesse and his family and their open-hearted generosity. In those brief twelve hours, we became friends. I wonder if they remember the two big-city girls who spent the night as fondly as I remember them.

Margaret Burk brings decades of performance, teaching, and producing experience to her storytelling programs and workshops. With a B.A. in Theatre and an M.A. in Communication, she taught theatre at Kennedy King College in Chicago and was a founding member of the Bread and Roses Theatre Company. From 1990–2002, she was Director of Development for the Chicago Sinfonietta and was named one of the "100 Women Making a Difference" in *Today's Chicago Woman* magazine.

After a career in arts administration, Margaret returned to her first love—the spoken word. She performs throughout the Chicago area, co-produces *Back Room Stories*, a monthly storytelling show, and is a board member of Illinois Storytelling Inc, which is a statewide association of storytellers.

Margaret believes in the power of story not only to entertain, but to touch the heart, spark the imagination, and embolden the spirit. She has three grown sons and four grandsons, and lives with her husband in Oak Park, Illinois. www.margaretburk.com

CHAPTER 14: KATIE BY JONATHAN EUSEPPI

My whole life, I felt as if there was a part of me that was broken and unlovable. My mindset was that you were a sucker for loving too much, and if you loved another person—or worse, yourself—that you should hide it from the world because you would end up getting very hurt and regret showing your true feelings.

That single thought ran through every part of my life, and I spent most of my time hiding. When I met Katie, something changed. I knew she was the one and I knew how much she loved me. And even if I didn't love myself, I wanted to protect her love. So when we started dating, I woke up every morning and looked into the mirror, saying: "I love and accept you exactly as you are. I commit to loving and accepting you fully to the best of my abilities." When I finally surrendered to the fact that self-love was the only way to make this work, I did so begrudgingly. There was a big part of me that was ashamed that I was so fucked up that I had to wake up every morning and talk to myself in the mirror. There was literally a voice in my head that yelled, "Well, I guess we are going to have to try this fucking self-love thing!"

At twenty-nine I wanted to date, but I had just gone through a rough patch, and if I met someone I wanted to take things very slow. My friends Leila and Katrina and I would talk exclusively about love and relationships. They would always say, "You should go out with our friend Katie. You both think the same and it would be a good fit."

It was fun to talk about dating, but when the reality of it presented itself, I would get nervous and say: "I have too much anxiety for that. I'm not ready to actually date someone."

Little did I know that months earlier Katie had seen me in a show and turned to Leila, saying, "That Jonathan Euseppi has a nice face."

Leila lit up: "Oh my God! Yes!!! You should totally go out with him!"

Katie wasn't as sure. "Calm down, I'm not saying I want to date him, I'm just saying he has a nice face."

Then one night I was leaving a bar and I saw Katie sitting at a table. I went over and asked, "Hi, Katie, how are you?" We ended up talking for a little while, and apparently that night something clicked for her. She made the decision to ask me out the next day.

She was at the gym, about to go into a yoga class, and casually composed a Facebook message: "Hey Jonathan, hope you're having a good week! I thought it'd be fun for us to hang out. Would you be down to grab a drink in the next week or two?" She told me later that it was an easy message to compose, but difficult to send. *Oh shit, I'm about to ask someone out.* She felt the fear rise up, so she took a deep breath and said to herself, *Be brave, be brave, be brave.* She hit the send button and walked into her class.

I was Uber driving. I saw the message and was stunned. *Oh my God!* I pulled the car over. *Katie wants to go out with me!* I was so excited that my heart filled up, but then I got scared. *What if I'm not good enough? What if I let her down? I have too much anxiety for dating!* I was spinning, so I called my friend Mike.

Mike listened to me and then said, "Jonathan, you are allowed to date people if you have anxiety! Just show up and see what happens."

"Oh yeah. I just go and see. That makes sense."

I hung up with Mike and casually composed a message. It was easy to compose, but when it came time to hit send, I stopped. *Oh shit. I'm about to actually go out with someone.* I felt the fear rise up, so I took a deep breath. *Be brave, be brave, be brave.* I hit send and started driving like there was no tomorrow.

Two hours later I got a message from her: "Alright, cool! Thursday works for me!"

Oh my God!!! I'm going on a date!

We ended up meeting at a bar in Andersonville called Simon's, and we talked about our families and ourselves for hours. When the date was over, I walked her to her Divvy bike and we hugged goodbye. We were taking things slow.

Then, two weeks later, we both fell head over heels in love! We had planned to go to a street festival called Midsommarfest. I went to pick her up at her apartment and felt an intense connection between us. It was summer and we were both wearing short shorts. We were both hot—physically and for each other. We tried to pretend that we weren't, but that just made things more intense.

I was sitting on a stool in the kitchen. She slowly walked over and stood right between my legs and we stared at each other... And then we had sex. It was very hot. Eye contact, emotion, not something that usually happens after two weeks. Right afterward, we were lying on our backs looking up at the ceiling, and eventually Katie said, "Well, that was intense."

We did go to the festival, but before we knew it, we were back at her apartment. We immediately took our clothes off and got snacks of cheese, crackers, and wine. It was so simple, so calming, it felt like complete freedom. I loved her then, but I didn't say anything out loud. We began to kiss, and she got on top of me and was looking at me deeply and I could see that she was struggling to say something. She shook her head and finally said, "So—I'm having a lot of feelings!"

"Me too," I said.

Tears welled up in her eyes and she said, "So I think I'm falling in love with you."

Oh no. We're not taking things slow at all!

"I just had to say it out loud because I felt it," she said.

"Of course," I responded.

But then the thought, *What if I'm not good enough?* reared its head and I fumbled with my words and said everything other than "I love you, too."

"You don't have to say anything about it. It would just feel inauthentic for me to go on and pretend when that is how I feel," she said.

The next day I thought about it, tried to remove my fear, and tap into how I actually felt. I sat with it for a while and then composed a message. It was easy to write but difficult to send. I felt the fear rise up, so I took a deep breath and willed my finger toward the send button.

"I'm pretty sure I went over this last night,"—*I totally didn't go over it last night*—"Do you know that I love you and you are kind of the best?"

She texted back, "I just collapsed."

So in two weeks we fell in love. We were not taking things slow, but don't worry, in six weeks—we got engaged! I know. We threw *taking it slow* out the window! Here's what happened. We went to our friend's Fourth of July party and quickly we found ourselves alone on a balcony. We were telling each other about our favorite YouTube videos and Katie said, "Have you seen the one with the old woman in the hospital bed and the old man is stroking her cheek, saying, 'My love'?"

I felt this intense feeling in my chest, and for the first time in my life I felt completely relaxed around someone. Tears rolled down my cheeks and I said, "No, I haven't seen that one." We headed back into the party, but I had to leave to go to a show, so I kissed her goodbye. I got into my car and before I did anything, I said out loud to myself, "I am going to marry her!"

Ten minutes later she texted me, "Have you accepted the fact that we are going to spend the rest of our lives together?"

I texted back, "When I got into the car, I accepted that fact."

She texted, "You did?!? I could have married you by date four, maybe date three? My heart is beating so fast."

I texted back, "Yes. I did!"

She texted, "This makes the most sense of anything ever. Welp. I guess that is what we are doing."

I texted back, "Yeah, nothing has made more sense."

She texted, "Okay. I'm going to start telling people."

I texted back, "Scream it from the mountaintops!"

And just like that: we were engaged.

Holy shit we're engaged?!!!

We're engaged!!!

She immediately took an Uber to the theater. When she got there, we ran to each other and kissed and deeply hugged. There was no getting down on one knee or anything like that because it wasn't one person asking the other; it was two people coming to a realization.

After the show we had celebratory drinks and I called Mike, who said, "Jesus Christ, I thought you were taking things slow?"

That night we slept at her apartment, but in the morning the enormity of what we had just done swept over me and I got scared and the fear rose up once more. The thoughts came back. *What if I'm not good enough? What if I let her down? What if she expects me to be a different person now?*

I rolled over and said, "I'm a broke comedian."

"I know," she said.

"And you still want to marry me?"

"Duh."

It turns out those thoughts weren't true. I was good enough. She saw me and loved me exactly as I was.

A year later we got married. I put my vows in my suit pocket. I couldn't even rehearse them because if I thought about the words I was going to say I would begin to cry. But as Katie walked down the aisle, my chest felt like it was going to explode and I started taking in deep breaths. Everyone in the room could feel the power and enormity of my love. I had hidden my love my whole life, and now in front of all of these people I was going to proudly declare it. I pulled my vows out of my suit pocket and said,

"My love, when I wake up in the morning and I turn over and see you there, there is this gratitude that fills me up and I almost don't know what to do, so I end up starting most days by kissing your back as many times as I can because I am just so grateful for you and your love. Your love is powerful and truthful, and it has this genuineness that I would do anything to protect. You exude this calming and playful energy, and you just being you blows me away. Last Sunday we were both so tired and you said, 'We should get Italian sandwiches.' And I wanted to yell, 'This is the best person I have ever met!!!' And we spent the whole day in our hot-ass apartment, in our underwear, watching *Rupaul's Drag Race*, laughing, having great conversation, and it was one of the best days of my life. We didn't have to do anything special because just being with you, in your presence, is the thing that is so special to me. Our relationship is this calming, fun, exuberant place that means more to me than anything. I am grateful to you every day, and I love you."

It turns out that hiding my love didn't protect me. Expressing it did, and as we walked down the aisle together, I was overcome with bliss.

Jonathan Euseppi is a storyteller, stand-up comedian, and improviser. He is best known for his storytelling style, which tackles intense subjects while holding them in a loving and humorous way. His one-person show *Grief is Horny* won the Staff Pick for Best in Fringe at the 2019 San Francisco Fringe Festival. He has performed stories at City Winery and the Gibbs Morrison Cultural Center. He recently completed a successful run on his one-person show *Cancer is Gorgeous* at the Crowd Theater in Chicago. When not performing, Jonathan enjoys spending time with his wife Katie and their tabby cat Orson.

CHAPTER 15: SUBBY BY ARLENE MALINOWSKI

David takes a hit off of the joint. "It'll be fast money." Inhale. "Good money." Inhale. "Easy money." Hold. Hold. Exhale.

It was just two days after college graduation and a few months before any job offers would come in. I was with David, my neighbor at Delaware Heights, a sublet in a college apartment complex. You know the kind: cinderblock walls, two couches passed down from some frat house, and a stereo system that cost as much as a year's tuition. David was finishing up a slow roasting MBA and we were in the luscious catch-and-release phase of a summer romance.

"If substitute teaching is so great, why don't you do it?" I counter.

"I've got a job."

"You're a drug pusher."

"I'm an entrepreneur, which means I'm using my degree while you're not."

Actually, David wasn't a drug pusher, just a dealer. There is a difference. Besides, in 1970s Jersey weed wasn't considered a drug. It was a beer chaser.

Every day David would make meatball hoagies using his mother's secret tomato sauce recipe. She said she was "the only Jew who could give those I-talians a run for their money." Her secret? Sugar.

Then David would tuck a little baggie of marijuana into the hoagie and wait for the order to come in: two meatballs, a nickel bag; three meatballs, a dime bag. You could get high, get the munchies, and have a sandwich right there. Best of all, David had the hoagie mobile and he delivered.

I take a hit off the joint and breathe in. He does the same. We breathe out together. He says, "When I crunch the numbers, you only have to work six days a month to cover your nut."

I whine. "It'll be a hassle. I don't have a car."

He smiles. "We've got the hoagie mobile." This mention thrills me, not for the promised rides but for the fact that he said "we," as in we are a couple. I could be a Sub, with the hoagie man by my side!

And he was right that teaching was my thing. I was good at it. No, great at it. When I was eight, I taught my dolls to read. In Sunday school, I taught first graders about being cast for all of eternity into the fiery pit of hell. And when I was a Resident Assistant, I taught college students how to break the rules and get away with it. I loved teaching. Teaching made me feel big within myself. To see people grow, and to know that you might have played your little part in that, gave me a high.

I file all the necessary paperwork—which consists of a measly two-sided application and a copy of my transcripts—with the Board of Education and complete my fifteen-minute interview. Fifteen minutes! I took cigarette breaks longer than that at the diner where I pushed burgers to college students too hungover to notice the ketchup was watered down. A few weeks go by and early one morning, while I am in the deepest level of REM sleep, I hear the phone ringing. The voice on the other end sounds tired. "This is the County Board of Education. We have a three-day job at Washington Elementary, fourth grade."

I go through my roommate Monica's closet and put on an Indian print wrap skirt, a black gauze shirt, and tan Candies—the ubiquitous high-heeled mules that looked like hooker shoes, which are great because if the teaching thing doesn't work out, I have the correct footwear for another job that is fast, easy money. This outfit, I figure, will make me look professional but cool, because I am going to be the Cool Sub.

These fourth graders are going to be hungry for knowledge —my knowledge—and not just for book smarts. I am going to be

Sydney Poitier in *To Sir with Love* (for everyone over fifty). I am going to be Mr. Katimski in *My So-Called Life* (for any gay boy who watched TV in 1994). I will be Coach Taylor in *Friday Night Lights* (for sports fans, millennials, and admirers of copious hair).

David picks me up in the hoagie mobile to take me to my first day and that's when it hits me. Oh my God! Good things NEVER happen to substitute teachers.

"David, I can't do this."

David reassures me, "You're going to be fine. You teach Deaf kids and that's gotta be a lot harder than teaching regular kids. Any idiot can do that."

I had done my student teaching at the New Jersey School for the Deaf. The campus had beautiful rolling hills and the students were sweet and inquisitive. I grew up in a Deaf family, so I understood the culture. I spoke sign language fluently, and that went a long way toward my acceptance and success. But now I am outside of Washington Elementary. There are no rolling hills, just a ten-foot high chain link fence surrounding an asphalt lot in an angry, broken part of the city.

"David! I can't teach. I'm not ready."

I had never let myself think this thought, but now it hangs suffocating in the air, and I know it is true. This is like knowing how to ride a bike with training wheels and then signing up for the Tour de France. Stupid!

Through the halls wafts the tangy smell of disinfectant and urine. My Candies clack clack clack on the linoleum floor as I scan the doors: room 110, 111, 112, and then my classroom. The bell rings. I adjust Monica's wrap skirt and go inside. OMG. There are at least thirty of them, maybe fifty, maybe more! I don't know! I smile and I breathe. They do not breathe with me.

"Good morning, I'm your substitute teacher today." I turn to write my name on the board in big loopy letters, Ms. Malinowski. "Alright, I'm here for three days and…" They begin to smile. I think, *Good, they're smiling, this is good!* Then they start to giggle and scream.

"Hey, Sub-bay," a kid in the back yells and pulls his shirt

out until it looks like he has an impressive set of boobs. I look down and see two white chalk circles on my breasts where I had brushed up against the blackboard. "Okay, okay. We've all had a nice laugh," I say, trying to look cool, trying to look like a sub who can take a joke. "Back to your seats." But they continue to holler and jump around. They look like a jar of shaken jelly beans. Malevolent jelly beans. "Enough. Stop please." Then, in my best Darth Vader voice, I bellow, "You in the blue tank top. I am your teacher. Tell me your name."

He stands. "My name is James, Subby."

"Hello, James, thank you for telling me about the chalk. Next?"

"My name is James."

"Wow, we have two Jameses. Next?" I point to a small, sweet-looking girl.

"I'm James."

I hate them! I hate this job!

The morning crawls by like a dehydrated triathlete. The kids roam around and drop pencils and laugh and laugh. There is a scuffle and even the goody-two-shoes who love helping the teacher are acting out. I yell, "Silence!" "Please stop calling me Subby!" "Sit down immediately!" and "Do you want a detention!" more times than I can count.

I am not being the kind or generous teacher I had always envisioned myself to be. This does not feel like fast money, good money, or easy money. The bell rings, and mercifully it's lunchtime. In the gyma/cafa/torium, the detention teacher informs me that I'm required to supervise while I eat. Back at the diner, when I realized I only got thirty minutes to eat, I quit my job. Lunch duty is a strange blend of relief from enemy fire and the hypervigilance of possible incoming.

I choose macaroni and cheese and balance my tray precariously on a windowsill so I can stand and maintain visual contact with the battlefield of orange chairs and bobbing heads. A calm comes over me as I sigh into the familiar comfort of Velveeta cheese. Nothing bad can happen with Velveeta. And that's when I see a quick undulation of bodies towards the corner of the room. *Oh for God's sake, now what?* Then I see a kid on the floor. One of the Jameses is on his back, flailing.

"Get a teacher," I holler. Nobody comes. "Get a teacher!"

Everything is happening fast, fast. It's all hands and feet and noise and James's lips turning blue.

"I'm not a real teacher! I don't know what I'm doing!"

I lie on floor next to him. "Take a deep breath!" I breathe. He doesn't breathe with me. More flailing. I grab him around the middle and squeeze as hard as I can, and a huge chunk of sandwich shoots right out of his mouth like a guy out of a circus cannon. I jump to my feet, like a gymnast in a perfect dismount.

"Did you see that? I'm a sub and I saved a kid's life on my first day." I say this to everyone and no one in particular, because the staff is focused around getting the throngs of students back to their tables.

The bell rings.

You have got to be fucking kidding me. I just brought a kid back from the dead like Lazarus, and you expect me to go back into that viper's pit? I know that, despite my heroics, all of this is a terrible mistake. I have no business being in this classroom or any classroom. I'm not cut out for teaching. How could I be so stupid? I'm not Hilary Swank in *Freedom Writers*.

After lunch, there are still three periods left and I'm so exhausted that I am sweating from every part of my body, but somehow I start to get my footing one tiny step at a time. I don't have to beg and threaten as much. I shout the *Detention* word less. I say "Thank you. Good job" a little more. And then it's over. The kids wave goodbye and they say, "See you tomorrow, Subby," and not in a mean way at all.

My feet ache in my hooker shoes, my black gauzy shirt has chalk all over it, and my skirt is covered with James's sandwich. I am fried. Outside I see the hoagie mobile.

"David, I think I'm a teacher!"

"Yeah, you are."

"No, no, no, you don't understand. I mean, I am a teacher, a real teacher. Thank God, I'm a teacher."

I take a breath and David breathes with me and in the quiet truthful part of my soul I *know* it's going to be a meatball night.

As an actor, playwright, and teaching artist, **Arlene Malinowski** views her solo work as an artistic extension of the social justice work she has been committed to for the last twenty-five years. She has created and toured work across the U.S. and internationally. Arlene is the recipient of a fellowship from the University of Illinois at Chicago's Department of Disability in the Arts, an LA Theater Ovations Award, and a LA Garland Award. She was a finalist in New Plays from the Heartland and a semifinalist for the O'Neill and Blue Ink Award. Two of her works were commissioned by 16th Street Theater.

She has also worked as an actor in film, television, and theater (Chicago: Goodman, Victory Gardens, 16th Street. LA: HBO Work Space, The Court, Blue Sphere). She's been a visiting artist for the Quad Cities Arts and Artist in Residence at 16th Street Theater. She is a Resident Playwright at Chicago Dramatists, where she developed and teaches the Solo/Story curriculum. As a storyteller, she has performed throughout Chicago. Her work appears in *Paramanu Pentaquark, En Posse Review, Huffington Post*, and the *Women of Letters Anthology* by Penguin Press. She is currently touring with her solo play, *Little Bit Not Normal*, which is designed to create dialogue around the subject of mental illness. arlenemalinowski.com

CHAPTER 16: MORNING RAIN BY DAVID BARISH

I am awakened early on a summer Sunday morning by a low rumble in the sky. I hear thunder, but it is not too close, too loud, or too threatening. I hear a hard, steady rain. I am not riled up but relaxed. I lie and listen to the rhythm. I'm feeling calm. The reminder of the natural world is giving me peace. The thunder gets softer and more distant, as I had slept through its approach. The storm is now making its way over the lake, leaving the downpour in its wake.

I lie listening, savoring this moment. I am listening for all the variations in the patterns of the rainfall. I drift from listening to the rain to thinking about it. I realize that I want to bottle this moment and keep it with me so I can recall it when I'm lying on my deathbed and need all the sweetest memories I can conjure to take me across to where I may be going. I don't know if I will be greedy, holding on fiercely to my remaining breaths, or whether I will softly let go with resignation and satisfaction. All I know is I will want to remember this.

I return from my remembering to the present and am again listening to the rainfall. I hear syncopation in the raindrops and am enjoying the concert. A hole in the gutter allows drops to hit a downspout. This adds an accent to the percussion. I focus on each raindrop I hear pelting the roof; the remnants of the bass-clef exhortations rumble low from the clouds. Why don't I see any streams of light from beyond the blinds? Where is the lightning? Perhaps over the lake? Again, I return and sense the present. I feel the air conditioning in my bedroom and a slight chill. I pull up the blanket and lie still.

I find myself once again thinking about the rain, rather than listening to it. I want to keep this moment for a time when I will need it. I am not on the verge of a personal or health crisis but think this rain has me feeling positively about my relationship with life, with my mortality, with my role in all of this. I am thinking of past moments that, like this one, made me feel alive and made me feel joy. I find myself stopping to recall and observe in the museum of memories. I tour some of the other images that make me feel human, that make me feel alive, that are as real as rain, that will comfort me when I am older and infirm. I am no longer hearing the rain. I am revisiting the past.

Why am I looking at this photo album in the yellowed pages of my memory? I think about when I turned sixty last year and said, "The math problem is inescapable," and that my time is limited no matter how much of it there is. I also can't escape the reality that I take a half dozen pills each day since heart surgery a number of years ago and after being diagnosed with diabetes. Because of these diseases, my cardiologist says I have a statistical depression on mortality. Do those statistical tables show my best-case scenario or an average? I have been increasingly aware that these moments, these rainfalls, this life, is mine now, but not for always. So I am savoring it.

I am driving a car on an interstate in Colorado with my wife sitting beside me and my adult children in the backseat recreating the silliness of their youth, poking each other and exclaiming that the other is touching her, giggling and guffawing, and eventually trying to outdo each other in telling the most vile "Yo mama" jokes to each other. All the while, said mama is sitting in front of them trying to salvage a little dignity, which throws the two of them into spasms of laughter they cannot control. I have to concentrate on the road so we can safely have this moment, and I want to support my beloved who is the butt of their jokes, but I am snickering under my breath while gently applying the brakes as I descend at seventy-five miles per hour in the Rocky Mountains.

I am lying on my back on the front lawn wearing my royal

blue Big Dogs shorts without a shirt. I have a big cast on my left lower leg while those same two women, who were at the time little girls, are jumping on me, taunting me for my inability to get up and chase them, and then moving my crutches away so I cannot get to them without crawling. I surrender and lie down, feeling the warmth of the sun and hearing the voices of little girls squealing and feeling a moment where they are more powerful than their dad.

I am on cross-country skis on a crisp Sunday morning in a forest preserve not far from the city when my friend points out an eagle flying overhead. We stop, ignoring our elevated heart rates and the frost on our faces, to observe this majestic and symbolic creature until it is no longer in sight, and then resume our striding across the snow.

I pull myself out of these memories, wanting to stay in the moment of this morning rain. I want to sense everything I can and just lie here. I do not want to work at this. I want to just be here and to feel this. I lie. I listen. I feel my wife's sleeping presence nearby.

The rain has stopped, but I still hear water dripping at a moderate tempo through the downspouts and am calm, listening to its music, while subconsciously aware that I want to keep listening to all of life's sounds, and seeing all of life's images, for as long as I can.

David Barish has been telling stories ever since his parents came home and asked him what had happened while they were away. He has been telling them in front of live audiences in the Chicago area since 2013, when he went to his first Story Sessions show and decided he wanted to tell his own stories. His stories have been published by *Story Club* magazine and *Stitch*. David is the co-host of *Do Not Submit Evanston,* an open mic for storytellers.

When he is not writing and telling stories, he is listening to them in his role as an attorney who represents injured workers and Social Security Disability claimants. His favorite way to arrive at a storytelling show, the office, or pretty much anywhere, is on his bicycle.

CHAPTER 17: MY DAD WAS A CAT LADY BY MARYA MORRIS

My dad was a cat lady.

And my mother was an enabler. We had *a lot* of cats in our house when I was growing up. My mom and dad would take in every stray cat that wandered in or was dropped off at our tiny ranch house in Madison. And unlike what you might expect today, they didn't rush them to the vet to have them spayed or neutered, because at one point we had twenty-two at once. That sounds awful in retrospect, but I don't remember thinking it was weird at all. It was kittens galore!

My dad always had a favorite cat. It was usually the cutest and bitchiest one in the bunch. He would double over laughing if a cat hissed at him. He loved their innate incredulity.

One of our cats was particularly finicky, always demanding to be fed but usually rejecting what was served. He was a gorgeous, fluffy, brown-and-black-striped Maine Coon kitten. I named him Maxwell, but within a couple of days my dad was calling him BooBoo. Somebody asked my dad how he got that name. He said, "*Look* at him. What else am I supposed to call him?!" When I started college and moved into an apartment, my dad would ride his bike over just to hang out with him. He didn't care if I was home.

When BooBoo was about eight years old, I moved into an apartment in Chicago with a roommate who was allergic to cats. BooBoo had to go back to live with my mom and dad, who also had moved to Chicago. Thus began what he labeled "The Friskies War." By "war" he meant a hand-drawn ledger that he posted on the fridge that listed every type of dry and wet cat food that he had bought for BooBoo with a check, check minus, or a question mark next to it, indicating whether he was willing to eat it. There was also a column for notes: "Took two licks, decided no," he penciled next to the check minus for Chicken Hearts in Gravy. Next to Cod, Sole, and Shrimp Paté he wrote, "Doesn't like the blends."

And nothing was ever BooBoo's fault. "That cat is a saint!" my dad would say. Once I was walking down the stairs and Boo-Boo was blocking my path and begging for my attention. I was carefully trying to tiptoe around him when he turned and sank his teeth into my foot. There was a lot of pain, major swelling, a trip to the ER, and antibiotics. My dad's comment: "What did you say that made him so mad?"

In 2005 my dad was diagnosed with Alzheimer's disease. About the same time, an orange-and-white stray cat started hanging around my parents' house. Eventually my dad lured him inside with Temptations cat treats. (He also once led a possum into the house the same way, thinking it was a stray Siamese.) He named the orange-and-white cat Rusty. Unlike BooBoo, who passed away in 2000 at age nineteen, Rusty was an extremely sweet and affectionate cat. He was also the kind of former stray cat who could not be kept indoors all the time.

As my dad's illness progressed, he became worried about Rusty's physical safety. When Rusty was out doing outdoor cat stuff, my dad was obsessed that he might get into fights or be hit by a car. In the winter he was afraid that Rusty's light-colored coat would blend into the snow and he would get hit by a snowplow. So he started following him. When Rusty went out, my dad went out. Up and down the sidewalk, between cars, down gangways, in the alleys, over fences, into the neighbors' backyards. Many of the neighbors came to know my dad and were aware he had Alzheimer's, so they weren't alarmed to see him on their front porch steps, sometimes napping, with Rusty asleep next to him.

While my dad was worried about Rusty getting lost or injured, my siblings and my mom and I were in a lingering panic that he was going to ride off and get lost. From the time he was about thirty years old into his seventies, he had ridden his bike at least

5,000 miles per year. He kept track of his rides, in miles and kilometers, in small booklet calendars he got for free from Hallmark card stores.

Even after his brain had deteriorated to a point where having a conversation or giving him any kind of instructions was a real struggle, he kept riding his bike. Bicycling was so deep in his muscle memory, so much a part of his everyday life, that he couldn't *not* do it. Alzheimer's, on the other hand, erased his common sense and his ability to tell hot from cold, north from south, night from day, and safe from dangerous.

On May 2, 2010, around two p.m., he left the house, alone, on his bike. My mom's fears went from worry to panic. She called me when he had been gone for about an hour.

The police put out a citywide BOLO—"Be on the lookout." My brother rode up and down the lakefront path. I drove every street and every route on every street that he had ever said was a good bike route. Halsted, Milwaukee Avenue, Leavitt, Loomis. The sun went down around seven p.m. By nine p.m. the temperature had dropped into the fifties. He was wearing a T-shirt, shorts, and Vans sneakers. We had a sick and helpless feeling. *Where could he be that he could not be found? Is he by the lake? Is he in the lake? Has someone intentionally hurt him? How is this going to end?*

Around eleven p.m. we got word that two cops had found him, walking his bike down the sidewalk in the Pullman neighborhood, twenty-three miles from home. When he was healthy, a bike ride of that distance was no big deal. The officers were blown away that he had ridden that far. We went and scooped him up at the police station at 111ᵗʰ & Vincennes. The cops were feeding him cookies out of the vending machine. Meanwhile, his mind had taken him back to his 1970 Vietnam War protester hippie self, asking loudly and repeatedly, "Hey, what are you pigs busting me for?"

By the end of 2013, my dad was in a nursing home. He was unable to carry on a conversation. He knew me as a familiar presence but mistook me for my mom or one of his former students. I showed him pictures of Rusty and BooBoo. He looked at the pictures but didn't smile.

Back at the house, Rusty went about his charmed life. Going in and out all day, enjoying his newfound freedom of not being followed by a helicopter dad. But late in October 2015, Rusty left and didn't come back. My mom was sick about it. I posted pictures of him all over the neighborhood. I got calls and texts from people who thought they spotted him. It was hard not knowing if he was alive or dead, but I was relieved that my dad didn't know that he was gone.

A couple of weeks later my dad came down with aspiration pneumonia, a common killer of Alzheimer's patients. Within two days he was in hospice. My mom was there around the clock, and my brother, sister, and I took turns going back and forth between taking care of their eight cats and sitting at my dad's bedside.

I spent the fourth night he was in hospice alone with him while my mom went home to shower and change clothes. It was about five in the morning when a nurse woke me up and told me my dad had no more than a few hours left, that I should call everyone to come back. But before I could dial my mom, she was calling me:

"Rusty just came home! He's all banged up and his tail is mangled, but he's okay. He's alive."

"Mom, dad is about to die. Come now."

I reject the notion that everything happens for a reason. And I'm not entirely sold on karma, although I hope it exists. I know for certain that a cat can't replace a father or a husband of fifty-eight years. But Rusty's timely homecoming felt like much, much more than a coincidence. In my moment of despair, this dirty, injured, and spooked cat, who mirrored my dad's kindheartedness and wanderlust, came home to give me hope that we would be alright.

Marya Morris is a storyteller, a freelance writer and editor, and a producer at Story Jam. She is a two-time Moth GrandSlam winner and has performed in many storytelling shows in and around Chicago since 2015. In her prior professional life, Marya conducted public policy research on urban planning issues and has published dozens of monographs and articles on land-use planning, transportation, urban design, public health, and afford-able housing.

She grew up in Madison, moved to Chicago after college, and now lives (under one roof!) in Wilmette with her husband, her mother, her in-laws, and usually at least one of her three chil-dren, who are at various points on launch trajectory. Marya holds a Master's in Urban and Regional Planning from the University of Illinois-Chicago and a Bachelor's degree in Economics from the University of Wisconsin.

CHAPTER 18: PUERTO VALLARTA BY STEVE GLICKMAN

It's Christmas Eve in 2005 and I am packed and ready to go to Puerto Vallarta. My suitcase waits by the front door. My flight leaves at nine a.m. on Christmas Day, and I cannot wait to get out of Chicago.

It's been an awful year. I broke up with my boyfriend of seven years and I've been in a fog ever since. I lost my mojo, my school spirit, my ability to sleep through the night. I almost lost my job due to my "lack of focus," as my boss said. But somehow, I made it to Christmas Eve and I am ready to reboot my life, starting now.

I cannot wait to get to Puerto Vallarta, lie down on that beautiful beach, order myself a piña colada served out of a coconut, and kiss this awful year goodbye. Farewell, snow and ice and wind-chill factor. Adiós, Chicago. ¡Hola, Mexico!

I am packed and ready to go. All I need is my passport. I look in my desk drawer, but it's not there. I look in my file cabinet, but it's not there. I look in my dresser drawers, my bedroom closet, the kitchen cabinets, but it's not in any of these places.

"Where the fuck is my passport?" I say to nobody, as I live alone. My flight leaves in just twelve hours.

Then I panic. I ransack my apartment, going from room to room, emptying every drawer, every closet, every cabinet, throwing the contents onto the floor where I can see it all clearly. I'm down on my hands and knees, sifting through the piles of stuff like a crazed burglar. And, after turning my apartment upside down—nothing!

"Where the fuck is my passport?!" I yell at the living room walls. I'm sure my neighbors can hear me—the walls are thin and it's almost midnight. They're probably calling the police right now. I don't care.

And then I get an idea. My passport must be at the office downtown. I must have left it there.

I grab my winter coat, jump in my car, and race downtown. The streets are deserted in the Loop on Christmas Eve, and I park right in front of my building. I run into the lobby, and the security guy gives me a puzzled look as I'm signing in.

"I lost something, and I think it's in my office," I say.

"Okay, well... Merry Christmas."

"You too!" I reply as I bolt to the elevator banks.

I take the elevator to the tenth floor. The lights are off, it's dark and silent. I race through the maze of cubicles like a trained rat on a mission. When I get to my cubicle, I ransack it. I pull out every drawer, every file cabinet, and dump the contents onto the floor. I sift through the piles of stuff on my hands and knees. After I've made a complete mess—nothing!

"Where the fuck is my passport?!" I yell to the empty office.

The truth is, I have no idea where it is, and I have no place else to search. Sitting on the floor of my office cubicle sometime after midnight, I stare into the darkness and try to compose myself. Then I say out loud, as calmly as possible: "I've lost my passport. I've looked everywhere I know of, but it's gone. I am not going to Puerto Vallarta for Christmas." And then I cry.

* * *

The next morning, back in my apartment, I make a pot of coffee and survey the mess. Then I spot my suitcase, still packed and waiting by the front door. "Merry Fucking Christmas," I mutter.

I contemplate how I will now spend Christmas week in Chicago. I can't visit my family, they're not in town. I can't visit my friends, because they all think I'm in Puerto Vallarta ... and that's what I want them to think. I boasted to everyone that I was going to spend Christmas on the beach in Mexico, and they could all have their white Christmas in Chicago, thank you very much.

I told my co-workers. I told my volleyball team. I told George, the star hitter on my volleyball team, who is a dreamboat and whom I have a crush on.

I can't fathom telling them I lost my passport. I just can't. I'll never hear the end of it. I feel like the biggest loser ever. My life was supposed to turn around, starting today. I thought I had hit rock bottom, but now it seems the bottom has fallen out and there's more rock bottom.

And then I get an idea.

I hide out in my apartment all week long. I spend my time watching movies and reading Mexico travel blogs. When I leave the apartment, I wear sunglasses and a hoodie, because I'm incognito. I leave for only two reasons: to go to the grocery store, or to the tanning salon.

I love the tanning salon. I love lying on the tanning bed in my Speedo, groovin' to my playlist, surrounded by the gentle warmth and humming of the UV lights as they slowly cook my skin to a deep golden brown. When I close my eyes, it feels like I'm lying on that beautiful beach in Puerto Vallarta.

Days pass. The first week in January comes. We have volleyball practice. I show up at the gym, armed with a deep tan and stories from the Mexico travel blogs. There are six courts going and I scan the gym for my team. Then I spot dreamboat George.

I'm nervous. Part of me wants to turn around, walk out of that gym, and go back into hiding for the rest of winter. But I know that won't solve anything. I know I have to get out there and live in the world, meet people, and take risks, even when I don't feel like it. That's what all the self-help books say.

So I walk up to dreamboat George with a smile on my face. He smiles back and asks, "So how was Puerto Vallarta?"

I say, "Muy bueno! The weather was perfect. The beaches were fantastic. And oh! The food ... so mucho delicioso!"

As I'm talking, I'm thinking, *Is he buying this bullshit?* I study his face for signs of doubt, and I can't really be sure, but I think he might be.

While I'm talking with dreamboat George, my other team-mates gather round and I repeat the story for them. With each retelling I grow more confident. I add more details; a snorkeling trip, a sunset cruise, dancing 'til dawn. Suddenly I realize I'm actually pretty good at this.

Dreamboat George says, "I'm so jealous!" Which are the words I long to hear. I simply smile and nod.

The next day, I go out to lunch with my boss and co-workers and I tell my story with confidence and panache as they listen and nod with obvious envy. As I'm telling my story, I'm actually starting to believe it myself.

* * *

I sat on this secret for eleven years.

Over time, I got my self-confidence back. I got a new passport, and I got a new boyfriend. We've travelled together, mostly beach vacations, but never to Puerto Vallarta because I don't like to repeat.

Last December, I was cleaning out my bedroom closet over the holidays. I spotted a ratty old jacket way in the back and I reached in and pulled it out. Just as I was throwing the jacket in the trash, I felt something hard in the breast pocket. Curious, I reached into the pocket and pulled out my fucking passport.

◆ ◆ ◆

Steve Glickman's stories have been featured on *The Moth Radio Hour* national radio broadcast and podcast. He's performed at the Laugh Factory, City Winery, and many other Chicago venues. He hosts the monthly storytelling show *Do Not Submit* in the Edgewater neighborhood. He's performed with the Piven Theater, Tellin' Tales Theater, the Evanston Storytelling Festival, This Much Is True, Story Sessions, You're Being Ridiculous, First Person Live, Story Jam, Story Club, Truth or Lie, Tenx9, and other storytelling shows in Chicago.

By day he's a software engineer. He earned his bachelor's degree from the University of Illinois-Urbana with a major in computer science and a minor in music. He lives in the Uptown neighborhood of Chicago with his partner Mark and their imaginary dog Ruffles.

CHAPTER 19: IT'S A SHAME
BY ANNA TUCCOLI

I remember receiving a phone call when I was about twenty-five years old from my mother, who lived in California, while I lived in Syracuse, New York. Not one for subtleties, she cried into the phone, "We just had to put Jim away. He's in the nut-house!" She went on to tell me that, Jim, my older brother, was on a psychiatric ward and had been diagnosed with schizophrenia. I was so stunned and devasted I did not tell my husband for days. I didn't tell anyone else for seven years.

The origins of my shame about my family are sometimes fragmented memories, but I do remember some of them from about the age of four. I remember musing, as I sometimes did, under my mother's ironing board, making kitchen floor angels, and asking her, "Mommy, what makes you so sad? Sometimes your face looks like an open watermelon, so red and juicy with tears." No answer.

I lived with my family in a little two-bedroom clapboard white house with brown trim in Oakland, California, from birth to eight years old. My father was a white-collar professional selling life insurance to poor, working-class families. When the collections fell off and he could no longer squeeze the nickels from his customers, he traded in his suits for railroad overalls at the Southern Pacific.

My mother never worked outside the home, always a fixture there, not venturing too far from our block. She was a troubled, artistic, agoraphobic, blonde athletic beauty in her younger years and an alcoholic later in life.

My brother Jim, three and a half years my senior, was a

severe asthmatic. He was rambunctious, bright, challenging, and difficult in every sense of the word. At times he would lead other children into trouble. He gave my parents a run for their money and plenty of worry.

Summers in northern California are rarely that hot, but tinderbox dry. The creeks run mostly dry; a trickle of water supplies enough liquid for tadpoles to swim and their parent frogs to survive off flies and insects. Children were often down in these creeks away from adult supervision. Eucalyptus trees and oaks provided shade for kids and sometimes transient alcoholic bums.

Not far from my house on Novelda Drive, down half a block, was San Leandro Creek. It was considered a somewhat forbidden place by adults due to its lack of visibility, but nevertheless was an alluring gathering place for children. Kids like my brother would lie and create cover stories to play in this mostly benign place.

One unusually hot summer day, Jim and Bobby Muller from across the street lied to their respective parents and went down to the creek. A familiar old man who was a wino was sitting down at the creek. He was well-known to the children and had befriended many of them the year before. He sat with his bottle of rotgut port, secreted in a paper bag, and sang songs, told stories, and played the harmonica. His stories were entertaining. He told one about riding the rails from Sacramento to the San Joaquin Valley and all the way to Oregon. He offered to help the boys complete a tree fort they had secretly been building.

Jim came back late in the afternoon. He was strangely quiet. He complained of yet another asthma attack and laid down in our shared bedroom.

Mrs. Muller called. My mother kept saying "no" into the phone. She cradled the phone for a while even after Mrs. Muller hung up. She banged open our bedroom door and screamed at Jim to wake up.

I cowered on the stiff green couch. Suddenly my cartoons weren't so interesting. I wondered what Jim had done now. Did he get into a fight? Not unusual. Did he tell some kid he could fly like Superman if he jumped off the roof with his cape on? Well, maybe. Did he swear at an adult? That must be it.

I stared out the picture window toward Bobby Muller's house. A black-and-white police car pulled up to the curb. The police went to Bobby's house and Mrs. Muller let them in. Then they came over to our house. The neighbors came out on their front porches and stared at Bobby, his mother, and eventually at my mother when she answered the door.

I heard strange words, "mollelsoned"? I was four years old and that word had no meaning. I sank in my seat with fear. I heard enough of the conversation to understand that a bad man had done something to the boys. Jim said nothing. Finally, they left. He threw up and then said the man had a knife and would kill him if he revealed what had occurred. I asked my mother what was wrong, why was everybody so mad? I was ignored and told to go watch TV.

Bobby provided a description of the man. I imagined a monster, half-man half- amphibian, with a knife rising out of the creek water. How could they have survived that? They were brave to fight the monster. Weren't they heroes?

The police searched. I stood at the window watching. The neighbors searched. The man had disappeared and I'm not sure if they ever found him.

The incident was never mentioned again. Vanished, banned from any discussion. Mrs. Muller forbade Bobby to play with Jim ever again. They became bitter enemies, which was fueled by their parents' venom. All of our fates were sealed by shame and stigma.

The San Leandro Creek still meanders through that part of Oakland, harboring tadpoles and frogs and sometimes monsters of the human kind, shaded by eucalyptus trees and oaks. The freights still ramble through there and the little house on N-ovelda Drive still looks as it did all those years ago.

The phone call I received when I was twenty-five years old from my mother silenced me for seven years, but thanks to the encouragement of a social worker friend, who saw potential in me, it also later led me to a graduate degree in social work. I didn't know it then, but I would have an over thirty-year career as a social worker trying to help others who deal with silent shame. During that time, I spent much of it working with children, some with trauma like Jim, to better understand its shadowy depths and to help those with stigma, shame, guilt, and mental illness.

Jim's life was difficult. When my mother died, my husband and I were able to bring him to Chicago. Although the transition was sometimes fraught with utter frustration, we were able to find support services for my brother that improved his quality of life and independence, including a job. Jim remained silent on this childhood incident for his entire life. Mainly he struggled with the symptoms of schizophrenia, now thought to be a genetic disorder, but beneath that were the unacknowledged effects of this trauma. As he once said to me, "I learned to embrace this thing, this life, Sis. Thanks."

As a social worker, **Anna Tuccoli** is no stranger to listening deeply to the stories of others. In fact, she calls them the "greatest stories never told." She is a Licensed Clinical Social Worker and holds a master's degree in Social Service Administration from the University of Chicago. In her over thirty-year career, she has worked as a school social worker, an administrator, a child welfare consultant, and a therapist for children and families, and has worn many other hats. Although born and raised in northern California, she has spent more than half her life living in Chicago. She is semiretired and works as a Social Work Consultant for a child welfare agency. Anna volunteers for three nonprofit organizations that work with children in the areas of literacy and nature education. In addition, she enjoys taking art classes, writing, exploring nature, and reading. She also adores her daughter, Elise, a dedicated special education teacher. She resides in lovely Lincoln Square in Chicago with her husband, a dog, and her twenty-year-old cat.

CHAPTER 20: CERTES CAPITAL BY CARMENITA PEOPLES

Is this my dream job? The company is called Certes Capital. *Certes*, meaning "in truth or certainty." I was intrigued!

It started when I was thirteen: I saw an Oscar-worthy film that captivated me called *Trading Places,* with Eddie Murphy and Dan Aykroyd. Eddie Murphy's character, Billy Ray Valentine, was given the opportunity to become a commodities broker. He and Dan Aykroyd ended up cornering the orange juice market and making millions. That movie changed my whole understanding!

My mom was always a wonderful supporter of my dreams, and she sent me on a special field trip with one of her friends who worked at the Chicago Stock Exchange. Knowing I needed to look the part, I wore a navy blue suit that day. During the tour we came across a huge panoramic window that overlooked brokers trading below. I couldn't hear anything, but felt tremendous exuberance and excitement, just like in the movie *Trading Places*. My tour guide gave me a friendly warning about the high stress levels and how brokers did nefarious acts to keep their energy up. Completely mesmerized as I watched the mostly white men jump up and down with flailing arms and waving slips of paper, I saw myself. I can do this. I was sold!

I went back to school with a new focus and drive; this girl was going to be a stockbroker! It was only a matter of time. I naturally shared my dreams with anyone who would listen. And eagerly began a ritual of absorbing the *Wall Street Journal* while quickly morphing into Alex P. Keaton of *Family Ties*. I attended Hampton University a Historically Black University, in Virginia, where I studied finance and joined the Young Republicans. I was on a serious mission and know how the game is played!

After college, I married and had two beautiful daughters, but the marriage didn't last. So it was back to Chicago with my girls. I had to get a new start with work that was financially rewarding and mentally stimulating. And that's when my eyes danced … an ad in the newspaper, "looking to hire stockbrokers for Waterhouse Securities, and we will pay for your training." My dream of becoming Billy Ray was rekindled.

The ad turned into an interview which led to a job offer. I was in! Soon I'd be a broker screaming and yelling in the middle of the floor like I'd witnessed so many years ago as a teenager. Studying for and taking the Series 7 exam was beyond anything I'd ever attempted before. It felt like vomiting, diarrhea, and pushing out a baby at the same time! But luckily the *Trading Gods* showed mercy; I passed my various federal and state exams and became a fully licensed securities broker!

I started banging out trades for Waterhouse Securities, now fondly known as TD Ameritrade. It wasn't the roar of the trading floor but working from my cubicle alongside others that deeply satisfied me. We worked hard trading stocks, mutual funds, and options, but we also had an incredible amount of fun. We were always learning and I was an absolute sponge; studying the markets, the makers, and the masters. I was getting my second wind after starting over, and it resuscitated me. Now fueled with purpose, drive, passion, and an absolute belief in the work. I felt like a million bucks and savored the new experiences this provocative brokerage lifestyle was rapidly affording.

Things were going great until the day TD Waterhouse executives asked everyone to go to a vacant floor in our building. We were frightened and confused. The "suits" announced they would be expanding their operations, and in order to accomplish that, they would close the Chicago office. We were given twenty minutes to get our things and exit the building. With deactivated badges and deflated souls, we realized the life we enjoyed as the "Waterhouse family" was over.

How could I have been on top and suddenly slammed into

the abyss of unemployment? We received a respectable severance package and assistance in our transition, but I wanted the thrill of my life back.

It's crazy how trading places can work both ways. After a few months, I found another opportunity in the want ads. This company needed a licensed broker for an accounting firm that was looking to expand. They offered me an impressive compensation and work-life balance—before that was even a perk! And because my daughters were still young, I talked the company into providing me with a totally outfitted home office, where I'd work twice a week.

The name, Certes Capital, uniquely created to emphasize our integrity and commitment to serving our clientele. There was a large Grecian stone on the letterhead, totally obscene. A typical day in the office might entail discussing portfolios among accountants, attorneys, and the investment department, which was my area. The days were stimulating and productive. Our boutique firm served trust-fund clients and was making great strides. But strangely, after the holidays, I noticed my colleagues starting to disappear. First an accountant, then a paralegal, and then an attorney. Soon there was a skeleton crew of about seven, which was down from fifteen.

This restructuring occurred in order to become our own broker-dealer (B/D) firm. We had established services and support with a reputable clearing house already, but I worried whether such a small team could meet these new financial and legal obligations. We had to provide our own checks and balances now, while continually learning. The work was intense, and we pushed past our mental limits. There was a silent partner, a medical doctor, who put himself in the center of our transition even though he had no expertise in this area. He championed the ideal of becoming our own B/D and exerted pressure to adhere to strict deadlines.

After Certes Capital went live, we could secure new business and give our existing clients more investment options. The intense workloads began to bring new stresses and the office felt fragmented. Surprisingly, we held our own, with about $280 million under management, or so I thought. And then the partners hired a twenty-five-year-old kid to be the new CEO. This decision was alarming, and we wondered if he was someone's relative, which would have explained it.

As the first-year audit approached, we prepared to welcome the NASD (National Association of Securities Dealers) into our office for a couple days. During the audit week, I was scheduled to go to the office each day. The auditor was combing through files, and all was going fine until she was halted by something. We were on the second day of the audit, it was about two p.m., and she was almost finished when she asked the new CEO about some dealings in Michigan and Indiana. He casually said, "I dunno..." She took a short pause and asked the same question again, this time without the smile in her voice. He abrasively dismissed her question and maintained he didn't know because he was new.

The auditor transformed from Mary Poppins to Carrie in an instant. It was a bloodbath! She demanded that we pull every single client file, every client email, and every trade. We were so close to the end, but she extended the audit and examined every record.

The partners called an emergency meeting that night to manage the fallout from the auditor's report. The meeting was set for ten p.m. at night! This clandestine phone rendezvous included everyone except my superior, Steve the CFO.

Where in the good hell was STEVE??? He was an active partner and we maintained the trading for the portfolios. I believed he was trustworthy and we had great rapport. The meeting began and discussions started out well—and then shifted to having Steve take the blame for the problematic deals. They plotted about taking Steve's ownership shares and making him sell his home. They wanted to get Steve out and retain his clients. I was mortified! These were people I thought I knew. Why and how could this save the firm? I remained silent. And as soon as the meeting ended, I called Steve. He was appreciative of the warning but didn't seem shocked. He was grateful for my loyalty and told me to just play it cool at work tomorrow.

The next day I made a couple of attempts to log in to my account but realized I was blocked. The manager, Christina, came into my office to ask if I had spoken to Steve. She wasn't her usual sweet self; there was pain in her eyes. She said he had called his attorney and had an injunction placed on the firm so no business could be done. She directed me to sit at my desk and stare at a blank screen for the next eight hours. And she was serious. With her piercing look, I thought she knew I was the mole. I felt like I was being punished as she left my office.

I was not going to sit there for eight hours doing nothing. So I did what any other professional would do, I faked an illness. As I got ready to leave, I stuffed my work journal into my bag, which made it protrude grossly. My manager asked me what I was doing, and I told her that I wasn't feeling well that morning and had pushed myself to come in. I'd be taking a sick day.

I proceeded past my office into the Certes lobby and Christina came toward me and asked to check my bags. *What??* Now I KNEW, SHE definitely KNEW I was the mole! I refused and she positioned herself in front of the door to block my exit. Now, this lady had a small build and a heavy Cantonese accent. I'm a buxom woman and had no time to play. We had a small stare-off and I pushed past her and started walking briskly to the exit of the large office building. She ran behind me screaming to the security guard, "Stop her, stop her!" The elderly black man looked shocked and surprised. He got up to block the door but I implored his help as I desperately sighed, "Brother." He let me pass and I ran at full speed across the two parking lots to the Metra station.

The firm was at odds now, and Steve and I were both on the outs. However, he was an owner and I was a mere employee. Another owner of the firm placed negative comments on my trading license, which *confirmed* that they knew I was the MOLE. A week after the incident I was let go without severance.

A few weeks later NASD informed me that all my trading was satisfactory, and I was removed from the investigation. The auditor asked if I would be a witness for the NASD, which would also benefit Steve. Apparently she discovered the company was making unaccredited land deals in Michigan and Indiana. It was "Dr. Greedy," the invisible partner, who was forcing the deals and who kept his hands clean because he was a "silent investor."

I went into the arbitration room for the hearing armed with my work journal. The stenographer, who was also a black woman, asked how I got tangled up in this mess? I shook my head and laughed, "Shady monsters." The questions shot from the defense, and I calmly and confidently countered with times, dates, and reasons. Steve and I were both cleared of any malice.

Luckily I was able to land at JP Morgan Chase Bank doing banking and investments with a few former colleagues from TD Waterhouse. It was like getting some of the old gang back together, but nowhere near as fun. When I think back on that time, my *Trading Places* dreams came full circle, just like they did for Billy Ray Valentine. And I'm grateful not to have ended up in a cell with Martha Stewart!

Carmenita Peoples is an artistic performer, writer, and certified Montessori educator. She works with students in grades K-12 in Chicago Public and Charter Schools, and in parochial and private institutions. She currently serves as a part-time staff and educational contractor at the University of Chicago Lab Schools. Her company, Innovative Art and Education, LLC, works with students, parents, and teachers to offer specialized programming, education, and support. As a graduate of The Second City Training Center musical conservatory, improv, and writing programs, Carmenita uses her artistry to connect and bridge inter-cultural and generational gaps.

A dreamer, a seeker, a mother, and a friend, Carmenita can be seen "edutaining" audiences throughout the city of Chicago, its surrounding suburbs, and online throughout the world.

CHAPTER 21: SEPTEMBER WEDDING, A 9/11 STORY BY JH PALMER

That morning as I rode the Red Line from the north side of Chicago to the Grand Avenue station downtown, I wrote in my journal about the countdown to my impending wedding: "Just four more days." When I got to work, my colleagues were clustered in the reception area, eyes glued to the TV, the World Trade Center up in smoke. I knew that instant that my wedding would, at best, be postponed. I called my mother in tears before the first tower fell, sobbing openly within the flimsy confines of my cubicle. My hometown of New York was reeling, my wedding was ruined, and I didn't give a damn who heard me cry. Work closed early, and I got a ride home in the backseat of a colleague's car. Traffic was heavy; I cried the whole way home. I sat on my couch, turned on the TV, and didn't move for hours.

I felt an overwhelming urge to take every last penny that my fiancé and I had saved for our honeymoon and send it to the Red Cross, keeping just enough to get on the next Greyhound bus bound for New York to volunteer to do whatever I could. My fiancé convinced me not to send *all* of our money, and the talking heads on TV convinced me that unless I had a specific service that I could offer—emergency psychiatry, for instance—that I'd be a burden arriving in New York at that particular moment. In the end I gave $300 to the Red Cross and stayed in Chicago and cried. I cried at home, I cried openly in the streets, I cried in the shower. On September 15, 2001, which should have been my wedding day, I woke to a gorgeous blue sky and a perfect sunny day. My fiancé went to work. Someone asked when we were getting married. "Our wedding was supposed to be today," I said.

As it happened, we had been legally married by Judge Lambros J. Kutubris a few months earlier, because my health insurance required that if I make any changes to my coverage, that I do so during the month of June. At the time it was a lark; we went to the Cook County Courthouse on a workday during my lunch break, fully expecting the experience to be unremarkable. Judge Kutubris could not have been more serious in his duties, speaking to us with gravity about the seriousness of marriage, that it is not a contract to be entered into lightly, and would we be exchanging rings today? Outside the courthouse we walked past a man with a Polaroid camera. "A picture of the happy couple?" he asked. "Five dollars for a beautiful memory." We declined, thinking that there would be plenty of time for wedding photos.

What had seemed like an exercise in cutting through red tape was now soothing my battered soul; no matter what happened now—if war broke out tomorrow, if Chicago was the next city to be terrorized, if familiar names were among the dead and missing—we were married.

Our wedding, which, up until that moment, had been more important than anything else I could think of, was no longer a top priority. No one was able to fly to Chicago, or anywhere else, and we were in no mood to celebrate. I didn't want the only topic of conversation to be the attacks, and I didn't want to have to remember, on every single anniversary for the rest of our lives, what else had happened that week. We made phone calls letting people know our decision; the most difficult one was to my fiancé's grandmother in Delavan, Wisconsin. She had been the real reason behind planning a wedding; any time we felt like throwing in the towel, eloping to Vegas, and leaving it at that, we'd think of how important this wedding was for her. She passed on the following month.

We indefinitely postponed. Our caterer refunded us in full, as did the airline that we had booked our honeymoon travel with. I love pie more than almost anything else in the world, and we had planned to have scads of homemade wedding pie instead of cake at our reception. My sister had an apple pie delivered to me at work the day we postponed with a note that read, "For a wonderful sister and a beautiful bride." I cried again and ate the whole thing in one sitting.

In our apartment on September 12, my fiancé and I sat next to each other on our well-worn couch, watching the news. My wedding dress and his suit hung in the bedroom closet, a chart with table seatings leaned against a wall, and our wedding rings rested in the pillowy interiors of two ring boxes on the mantle. When I was a little girl I was fascinated with ring boxes, delighting in the satisfying pull and snap they made when my mother let me look through her jewelry and try it on myself. I'd never owned a piece of jewelry that merited its own box, and had spent what seemed like hours opening and closing the boxes that held our wedding bands as I waited for the day we would stop looking at them and start wearing them. As we sat together watching the unrelenting images of destruction stream from the television, something took hold of me. I stood from the couch and walked to the mantle, picked up the ring boxes, and returned to the couch. I opened the one that contained my fiancé's ring.

"Give me your hand," I commanded softly.

"What are you doing?" he asked, tears filling his eyes.

"Give me your hand," I repeated. He held out his left hand for me, and I slipped the ring, a simple piece of jewelry made from white gold, onto his ring finger. "Michael Dalton Palmer, I take you as my husband," I said. "Now you," I said, handing him the box that contained my ring. He took my hand and slid the antique platinum ring next to the matching engagement ring that I'd been wearing for almost a year.

"Jessica Hilary Cohen, I take you as my wife," he said.

"Now we're married," I said. We kissed and settled back into viewing position, waiting to see what had become of our future.

Several months later we rescheduled our celebration to June 8, 2002, the anniversary of our Cook County Courthouse wedding, and we got to wear our wedding finery, have photos taken, and eat pie with invited guests. It resolved the anguish of having to postpone, but when asked how long we have been married, I always count from that courthouse day. Some anniversary dates can be pointed to in advance, and some happen without the weight of expectation.

JH Palmer is a Chicago-based writer and performer. From 2012–2017 she produced the live lit show *That's All She Wrote*, and she has performed at numerous storytelling and live lit events, including The Moth, 2nd Story, Story Club, Write Club, and You're Being Ridiculous. Her work has appeared in *The Toast*, *Story Club Magazine*, *Hypertext*, and *Thread*. She earned an MFA in creative nonfiction from Columbia College Chicago.

CHAPTER 22: THE WIZARDS MEET A LISTENER BY MICHAEL JERED KOPP

For most of the 1990s, roughly a decade after I got my real degree somewhere else, I took one class each semester at Northeastern Illinois University just to keep my time slot on their weird little student-run radio station. Since 1974, WZRD has broadcast an eclectic mix of unusual, underplayed, and wonderfully strange music unlike anything you will hear on other college radio stations. With only one hundred watts at 88.3 FM, the station reaches a small but incredibly loyal audience on the north side of Chicago. WZRD's dedication to utterly unique programming has forged a bond between the station's listeners and the DJs, a kinship fueled by an unquenchable thirst for the exotic.

I had been a WZRD listener since high school. There's a long history of listeners like me becoming DJs. I didn't know any of them by name when I came to the station, but that, it turns out, was by design. At WZRD, one of the few rules is that DJs cannot say their name on the radio. You're just another Wizard. That's what everybody calls the station: the Wizard. Another rule is that you can't do an all-punk, all-jazz, or all-electronic music show—you have to mix up styles and eras into a free-form mishmash where listeners never know what's coming up next.

Once I began my Wednesday eight-to-midnight shift, I became part of a family of brilliant oddballs, each of us with our own strong opinions about music and every other topic. This place wasn't just a radio station; it was a haven for like-minded outsiders to find one another. Our backgrounds and ages were as varied as our tastes in music: Kurt was an antique-book dealer,

Melissa worked as a pastry chef, Gary was an attorney, Ann a special ed teacher, and Lou was a high school janitor. There were marriages among Wizards, and many of us became lifelong friends. Brian, who is an electrical engineer and was the station's music director, still comes over to meticulously align the new stylus I've bought for my turntable. Annette, who worked at the East Bank Club, is now my Pilates trainer at a small studio. And not surprisingly, she always plays great music for our workouts.

Despite never saying our names on the air, each of our shows was a reflection of our unique personalities. Wizards picked their own music and looked at the new-release shelves, which were filled with wonders from tiny labels and local bands, as merely a suggestion. If you played something too popular, like a song you might hear on other radio stations, another Wizard might pop into the studio during your time slot to question your sanity. That happened once to me when I was playing a Stevie Wonder song. I segued into a track by MC 900 Ft. Jesus that used the same Stevie Wonder riff, and quickly proved I was a Wizard through and through.

Outside the studio and the solitude of our own shows, we Wizards had our own vibrant social scene. We had Wizard dinner parties, an annual Wizard awards ceremony, station fundraisers at local clubs, and a coffee house owned by a Wizard where we would hang out with listeners. There were outings to see Tuvan throat singers at the Field Museum, a ragtime-piano playing contest, and a Wizard camping trip in Michigan where we tried to keep the bears away by singing the only song we all knew, "Anarchy in the UK" by the Sex Pistols.

It was up to each individual Wizard to decide how they wanted to deal with the phone in the studio. Some DJs never gave out the number on the air and refused to answer the phone when it rang. Others, like me, enjoyed talking to listeners or giving out the occasional pair of tickets to a show at Lounge Ax or Club Foot. I loved my listeners, even the ones that rambled endlessly on the phone, because Wizard listeners were every bit as weird as the DJs. One of my regular callers was a guy with a deep bass voice who always wanted to hear the same obscure Johnny Cash song. When I did an overnight shift for a while, I would get calls at three am from an artist who had the Wizard on in her studio and wanted to hear a very specific set that included the Cramps, Frank Sinatra, Kraftwerk, and some Indian sitar music. You learned to expect the unexpected when the phone rang at WZRD.

One day, another DJ got a call from a long-time listener named Andre. He was calling from a local AIDS hospice. Andre was dying. Andre had a huge collection of rare music that he wanted to donate to the station, because the Wizards were the only group of weirdos he trusted with his records.

We picked up his collection and were instantly aware of the major role that music played in Andre's life: everything was in near-mint condition, well-loved but delicately handled. Andre had records we had only heard about in whispered rumors: imports where only one hundred copies were known to exist, LPs with hand-drawn covers, twelve-inch 45s you could only buy at live shows. This donation was an overwhelmingly generous one, worth many thousands of dollars, but only people like us at WZRD would appreciate its true value. And that is why Andre had called the Wizard.

None of us really got to know Andre. We never learned where he came from, what he did for work, or what inspired his passion for experimental music. He was already gravely ill during the one brief visit we had with him when we picked up his records, so there wasn't a lot of time to learn his story. Yet, through his collection, we all recognized that Andre was one of us, and that he'd be forever part of the Wizard family. Music has a way of connecting people like that.

Not long after our visit, Andre died, his final mission complete. Those of us who worked Andre's collection felt his loss deeply. For some, it was the first time they had known someone who had died of AIDS. For others it was a reminder; I had recently lost a close friend to AIDS, a fellow record collector who'd co-hosted my radio show a few times, so Andre's passing hit especially hard for me.

WZRD dedicated twenty-four hours of airtime to Andre, playing only music from his collection, and talking with local experts at the front lines of the health crisis. We also put a red ribbon sticker on every one of Andre's records, and left a sign on the music library wall to tell his story.

It's been years since I've done my show, but I still tune in to the Wizard whenever I'm in the neighborhood. Sometimes I hear something I recognize. Andre's collection is being played by a whole new generation of weirdos at WZRD today. Andre lives on.

Trained in college to be an advertising copywriter, **Michael Jered Kopp** made a conscious choice to use his powers for the forces of good rather than evil. A promising career writing restaurant reviews for a Chicago tourism magazine was cut tragically short when Michael ran out of synonyms for the word "delicious."

After discovering his latent skills as a technologist, Michael managed website development for Chicago's finest rock radio station, an infamous Broadway producer, and a New York City business school. Having confirmed his suspicion that economics professors may be the least funny people on the planet, Michael continued down the twisted path that inevitably led to storytelling.

CHAPTER 23: DELIRIUM
BY DEBBI WELCH

Where the heck am I? Where did that window by the side of the bed go? It was there when I fell asleep, I know it was. Where am I? In the Twilight Zone? Okay, take a breath, look around. What do you see? *Sky blue walls, a wooden glider, three paintings of people on the wall where that window should be.* I'm back in Chicago! I'm in my bedroom on Bradley Place. That window by the side of the bed that I was recalling was in our room at the Red Roof Inn in Ann Arbor last week!

My husband Joe and I had traveled to Ann Arbor, Michigan, to see his dad. We stayed at the Red Roof Inn. As always, when lying on the bed, there was a large window to the left. We stayed there for seven nights and then drove home. When I woke up that first morning back in Chicago, I was totally confused and disoriented.

I've experienced other events that have made me feel disoriented. When I left my home office in the basement den and walked up to the first floor, a walk that takes about sixty seconds, I couldn't remember what the hell I wanted, needed, or had to do when I got there. So I got angry, went back down to the basement to what I was doing, and tried to jog my memory.

Okay, I was sitting at my desk working through the basket of monthly bills. I remembered I needed to pay some medical bills as well, but those were in the other basket. I put my hand on that basket and thought about the eye appointment I was supposed to make. And that is when I realized I was on my way upstairs to find the eye doctor's phone number!

So I tried again. I went upstairs, repeating, "Don't forget, you need the eye doctor's phone number" every step of the way. I got that number and made that appointment!

I've also found myself running a board meeting and struggling to think of the word "contribution" when discussing our fundraising goals. I've introduced my niece, Meg, as my cousin in front of her father, her husband, and many other family members. I've scrambled to think of the name of my dear friend Juli, who is a woman I've known for twenty years and see at least three times a week.

These instances are quite annoying, sometimes embarrassing, and even frightening. Right now, they don't happen too often. But they're definitely a taste of what I imagine dementia and delirium might feel like.

That trip to Ann Arbor had been to visit my then-ninety-two-year-old father-in-law, Lyndon. I've known Lyndon for over thirty years and have always found visiting him to be joyful and interesting. Lyndon is a man who really listens. He actually leans in while you're speaking, and you never have the feeling he is just thinking about what he wants to say. He simply wants to hear your thoughts and enjoy the moment. He plays harmonica, and often the whole family—all fifteen of us—will join him in rousing renditions of "Oh Mary Don't You Weep" and "As I Walked Down the Streets of Laredo." Lyndon's concentration is remarkable, whether it's spending hours on end working on a jigsaw puzzle or playing chess for two to three hours with his grandson. He has a patience that many of us can only wish for.

We had just been to Ann Arbor because Lyndon had contracted a urinary tract infection (UTI). In the elderly, a UTI often does not have pain or bleeding, but often causes some dementia (a decline in mental ability serious enough to interfere with daily life). My father-in-law, a man who had entered Harvard at sixteen, had tried to put a bouquet of peonies in his fish tank. A UTI can also cause delirium, which results in confused thinking and a reduced awareness of the environment. Lyndon, one of the most honest and ethical men I have ever known, struggled with the EMTs, whom he thought were arresting him for money laundering. After he was brought to the hospital, he fought nurses re-peatedly even though he was introduced to them many times. "I can bathe myself. What are you doing?" "Get away from me! Who are you?" Convinced he was in a five-star hotel, he thought the food and service terrible.

From the hospital to rehab, the delirium continued. Once they began to get the infection under control and the bacteria left his system, Lyndon's mind started to return to normal and the odd behaviors began to disappear. We began to see glimmers of the gentleman I had known for over thirty years. My husband went a couple of days ahead of me to the rehab facility. Upon my arrival, I was told that my father-in-law had insisted on remain-ing in a chair until I arrived, refusing to lay down and rest. He gave me a smile when he saw me, took both of my hands in his, and kissed each one. Later that evening, I convinced him to play his harmonica for us and one of the nurses, something he hadn't done in quite a while.

That wasn't the first time the dementia and delirium had occurred. Several months before this he had begun having trouble following conversations, at times wasn't sure where he was, and didn't always recognize friends and family members. We all thought we were entering a new era—and prepared for this to be his and our new reality. Thankfully, that first time a doctor dis-covered that the cause was a B-12 deficiency, and he prescribed a series of shots. There was a noticeable improvement after the first shot and we soon had our happy and in-the-moment Lyndon back.

I don't know how aware he was of what his mind did to him during these episodes. I do know how much more relaxed and happy he was when he recognized everyone, was able to get back to his home and do jigsaw puzzles for hours, and had a re-newed concentration to solve Sudoku problems with an intricate spreadsheet he developed and that only he could truly under-stand. Knowing that there was a visible end to the delirium and dementia-like behaviors was truly a gift. It was like, after shaking his head for a few minutes, he finally realized that he was at home and that the window he remembered had only been in his hotel room.

How many people in their eighties and nineties exhibit these signs of dementia and delirium and either have no family to watch over them or don't have physicians with geriatric training to recognize these illnesses? How many relationships are affected by not understanding that a loved one's behavior is due to a medical condition? How many seniors have these infections and their loved ones or doctors simply believe it's just old age? How many of these seniors could be living fuller lives? Would they have a more peaceful and enjoyable end of life?

So much of our lives are defined by our memories and our place within them, and by our ability to make and remember new ones. Our memories say where we came from and whom we came from, and they tell how we've changed and grown. Memories are how we learn what we like, what we won't tolerate, and what to look for in friends and lovers. When we have these memories taken away, stolen, how would we find our way home?

So I continue occasionally to forget that I wanted to make an eye doctor's appointment or I search for an elusive word while trying to lead a meeting, or fumble on the name of a dear friend, or struggle to locate that present I hid that should have been easy to find. But, thank goodness, I can still remember all those afternoons so many years ago at Friendly's Ice Cream drinking orange sherbet coolers with my best friend Karen, the doll birthday cakes my mom always made for my birthday, and the joy of seeing each of my children for the first time. And God willing, I will always remember my way home.

◆ ◆ ◆

Debbi Welch has been a storyteller and writer in Chicago for over thirty years. As a children's entertainer Debbi has appeared in many venues, including the Art Institute of Chicago, The Second City Children's Theater, and the Chicago Public Library, as well as in many public and private schools. She has performed her personal essays in Chicago, Seattle, and London.

Debbi is the immediate past-president of the Board of Directors of Young Chicago Authors, an organization that helps young people from all backgrounds to understand the importance of their own stories and those of others. She created and coordinated the Authors in the Schools program for the Chicago Near South Planning Board, bringing authors and their books into elementary schools across the city. As well, Debbi spent six years coordinating all of the children's programming for the Printers Row Book Fair.

Debbi is the proud wife, mother, and mother-in-law of accomplished poets, essayists, and nonfiction writers. She is looking forward to hearing and reading the words and stories of her grandchildren.

CHAPTER 24: MOM'S OLD CLOTHES BY ANNE E. BEALL

When my marriage ends in divorce, I find myself without a place to go for Thanksgiving.

My ex-husband and I no longer speak after he came to the house to collect some things he'd forgotten. "You're a fucking bitch," he screams repeatedly and so loudly that the neighbors can hear.

I'm also estranged from my stepchildren, whom I always regarded as my own kids and who have decided to take sides in this divorce.

I roam my house. Downstairs I walk past the small spare bedroom, with the multicolored blue quilt on a pristine white bedframe and matching white dresser. There are two of my photographs on the wall. But I don't see any of these things. I see my daughter sitting on her bed with her clothing spread everywhere, her guitar is nearby, books are on the floor, the walls are covered in various pictures and posters and notes from friends. Her room has a faint smell of oil paint, with her paints, brushes, and small canvases stacked against one wall. She's in mid-sentence talking on her phone and she's laughing. But when I go to talk to her, she disappears along with her things.

Across the hall is another spare bedroom. The bed is covered in a beige quilt that contains specks of blue, and it sits on a pine bed-frame that matches a wide six-drawer dresser off to the side. The queen-sized bed fills the small room and is at an angle to accommodate the angular walls. But that's not what I see. I see my son on his bed typing away on his computer, with a scratched dresser off to the right, a very low bed, clothes on the floor, bags of laundry, items strewn everywhere. His room smells a bit like dirty clothing, and I'm about to ask him if he wants to do his laundry. But as I begin to speak, he disappears.

I go upstairs, where my formal living room has reproduction antique furniture from the Victorian era and my dining room has a large walnut table that's been in my family for 150 years. Everything is tidy and neat, and my tabby cat is sleeping underneath the table. But for a split second I'm not in this time or place. It's my favorite holiday, Thanksgiving. The table has a burgundy tablecloth, navy placemats, shiny cutlery, and wine glasses. There's a large turkey, two different types of potatoes, cornbread, salad, three vegetables, a quiche, and dinner rolls. Food resides on every space and the table looks small.

"You really outdid yourself this year!" My husband beams at the head of the table.

"Yeah Mom, thanks for the vegetarian quiche," my daughter says.

I start to say "You're welcome," but they all disappear. I'm sitting at my formal table, which appears enormous in its barren state. There will not be a Thanksgiving in my home and I currently have nowhere to go.

I call my sister and ask her what she's doing for the holiday.

"Well, I'm not sure. I think we'll be camping."

"Camping in November?"

"Well, I just know we're not going to be in town and I just think we'll be doing something like that."

There is a long pause.

"Why don't you call Mom?"

I hang up the phone.

How did I get to this point in my life where I have nowhere to go for the holidays?

The heaviness settles into my body. I want to crawl into my bed and forget who I am. I want to wake up in another life, where I have somewhere to go for Thanksgiving that doesn't involve a visit with my mother.

When I think of her, I feel tension in my chest, followed by a tingling in my arms that makes me want to reach out, take a mallet, and smash everything in sight. She is not maternal. I recall that when I was much younger, I framed one of my floral photographs and sent it to her for her birthday.

"Did you receive my gift?" I asked expectantly.

"Yes, I did. It's good. Almost as good as one of my photographs."

My mother has been asking me to visit for a while. I don't want to go. Being with her tends to agitate me, because it reminds me of how this and other relationships in my life don't work.

I'm told by my father that this relationship didn't work in the early years. I was a very independent child who resisted parental help. When I was learning to walk, I would crawl out into the middle of the floor and try to stand up. When I was unable, I would become distressed and my mother would approach and say, "Let me help you."

"No! Annie can do it!" I'd yell loudly.

Years later, she tells me that my problems in life are due to this relationship.

"Your problem is me," she states without emotion.

I'm not sure how to respond so I say nothing.

I get on a plane to go visit her in Portland, Maine, for Thanksgiving.

"In case of an unexpected landing, an oxygen mask will fall from the compartment above your seat," the flight attendant says in a singsong voice.

Can it drop now? I feel I'm going to hyperventilate.

I begin reading a book that says you should challenge your beliefs because they become self-fulfilling prophecies. So I approach the visit as if she isn't my mother, but just a person who has invited me for the holiday.

On Thanksgiving Day, I wake up feeling thankful because I'm not alone. "We're going to have dinner with your stepbrother Shawn, his wife Danielle, and their kids," my mother declares when I go down to breakfast. "They're making dinner and they're excited to see you."

When I see Sean, he has the most welcoming smile. "Hey, thanks for coming!"

"Your mom gave me your book and I read it," Danielle exclaims. "She's very proud of you."

I thank her and realize this is the first time I've heard that.

The day, the meal, and the people are better than I expected.

The day after Thanksgiving, I sit with my mother at breakfast. "Hey, your closets in the guest bedroom where I'm staying are overstuffed. Do you want me to help you organize them?"

"Oh, I'd love that!"

We go to her two giant closets and I start pulling out each piece of clothing.

I hold up a blue silk dress and she smiles. "That was a Christmas present from your stepfather. I got so many compliments on this when I wore it. You know, this color might look good on you..."

"Do you think so?"

I don't want the dress, but I'm pleased that she wants to give it to me.

"And these are the pants I always wear when I paint. They don't fit that well any more ... but I made so many watercolor paintings with these," she says wistfully.

"Do you want one of my paintings?" she asks.

"That would be really nice. I'd love that."

I hold up a brightly colored skirt and ask: "How about this?"

"I bought that on a vacation in the Caribbean. We went down to see some friends and we ended up at this resort," she says, looking away as if she's actually still there. Then she reaches for a pink dress. "I wore this to your wedding. I'm so sorry that this divorce has been hard on you..."

"Yeah, it's been..." I break into tears and my mother puts her arm around me and I appreciate that.

We end up with a bunch of clothes that she's unable to part with, so I suggest she try each one. I tell her which things look good, what isn't in style anymore, and what is too worn or stained. We joke about how she resists every effort to get rid of each piece by saying she just wore it last spring. But we both know it's been years since she's worn many of these things.

We spend two days going through everything and end up with six garbage bags of clothing for Goodwill. In addition to the discarded clothing, we've let go of our disappointments in one another. I'm the child who still needs her and she's been interested and connected to me more than I realize.

As I leave for the airport, I turn to her. "I had a great time. Thanks so much for inviting me."

She replies, "Do you want to come for Thanksgiving next year?"

"Yes, let's do that."

Anne E. Beall is writer and storyteller who has published eight books on a variety of topics. She was recently interviewed on NPR about her book *Heroic, Helpful & Caring Cats*, and her book *Cinderella Didn't Live Happily Ever After* was featured in *People Magazine*. Her other books include: *5-Minute Meditation Vacations: Magical Journeys with a Personal Message*; *Community Cats: A Journey into the World of Feral Cats*; *Heartfelt Connections: How Animals and People Help One Another*; *Reading the Hidden Communications Around You: A Guide to Reading Body Language of Customers and Colleagues;* and *Strategic Market Research: A Guide to Conducting Research That Drives Businesses.*

She has told stories all over Chicago in a variety of shows, including Story Lab, Ten by Nine, Is This a Thing, Soul Stories, and The Moth. She is the founder and CEO of Beall Research, a strategic market-research firm in Chicago. Originally from Massachusetts, she's lived in Chicago for over twenty years and enjoys walking on the lakefront, sampling dark beers, and listening to other storytellers.

You can learn more about her on www.AnneBeall.com

CHAPTER 25: RETHINK THE CELIBACY THING BY JUDI LEE GOSHEN

I had my first adult date at forty. Seriously. I met my husband when I was nineteen. At twenty we quit college, got married, had two kids, and at forty—we separated. We sold the house, split the money, and moved into our own places. But the divorce wasn't final. Some people thought it was too soon to date, because technically I was still married. But I didn't agree. I figured if he dated while we were in counselling to save the marriage, I could date while we waited for the papers to be signed.

It was August of 1999. The new millennium was just around the corner. Everyone on earth was Y2K crazy, afraid that all the computers in the world would be so confused by the year 2000 that they would shut down completely on New Year's Eve. But that frenzy paled in comparison to the chaos going on inside my head. It was time for me to start dating, but dating could lead to intimacy and intimacy could lead to sex and sex could lead to an STD and an STD, I was convinced, would lead to death, or worse —warts.

I felt like the sexual equivalent to Rip Van Winkle. I fell asleep in the '70s to Donna Summers's "Love to Love You Baby" and woke up twenty years later to find I was "Livin' la Vida..." alona. I was at an age where every part of my body was supposed to be screaming, "Do me. Do me now!" Instead, I chose celibacy.

So, if I chose celibacy, why did I start dating within weeks after moving out? That I can answer in one word. Revenge. I thought if the knowledge of The Ex-Hole sleeping with other women had torn me apart, then his picturing me with another man would rip him to shreds. *Win-win.*

I turned to Roxy, my best friend from high school, for advice. Roxy had not only remained single during my two decades of marriage, she had remained firmly entrenched in the past. She still had long hair with bangs and still smoked Marlboro Reds, always holding the cigarette an arm's length from her body, and after every puff waved her hands frantically to dissipate the smoke. That way, no one in the room would think that she was the smoker. Spoiler alert—*everyone* in the room knew that she was the smoker.

Roxy and I decided to meet at the annual Jewish Singles' Dance at Navy Pier that Saturday night.

I walked around the rooftop, and when I finally spotted her, she informed me that she had just met someone and they were hitting it off. *Hitting it off* was code for me to get lost. So I had to fend for myself—alone—at my first-ever singles' party.

I put on my best party smile to hide my RBF (Resting Bitch Face) and pretended that I was having fun. But every man who came over to me made me want to disappear. They all asked questions, so many questions, and most of the questions I should have been able to answer: "Oh, so you're divorced?" *Well, not really.* "What's your name?" *Now or next week?*

My life was so up in the air that I couldn't answer a straightforward question. And I didn't even want to try. Roxy was still talking to the guy she was interested in, and I didn't want to give up too quickly, so I gave myself a time-out and snuck away to look at Lake Michigan.

The party was on the eastern roof of the Pier, and the breeze coming off the Lake was chilly for late August, but in my daughter's new cream-colored jacket, I wasn't cold. However, the jacket didn't match my outfit: a royal blue tank top, black capri pants, and chunky black Steve Madden slides. But I was glad I was wearing it, because it set me apart from all the other women in their tank tops, black capri pants, and chunky black Steve Madden slides. *Am I in style, or do all us single (or soon-to-be-single) women look alike?*

After a while I donned my smile and returned to the crowd. A man came up and bombarded me with more questions: "Hi, what's your name? What do you do? Do you have kids? Are you willing to have more?"

That's when I realized: these men were on a search. They were interviewing women for a specific position: wife. I was in a marital meat market! Sure, it may have been kosher, but I had been a vegetarian far too long. Being a wife was the last thing in the world I wanted. Well, maybe death—and genital warts— those were the last things in the world I wanted—but getting married and raising children again was right up there. I felt cornered, boxed-in, and panic began to build. I had to get out of there, fast.

I quickly found Roxy, said goodbye, and left. I was angry at myself for having gone in the first place, angry with my friend for not hanging out with me, and I blamed my husband for putting me out there in the singles world.

I was grumbling to myself as I walked off the roof, down the stairs, and through the arcade to get to the safety of my car. As I mumbled my frustrations aloud, a man from the party sidled up to me and asked, "Hey, where are you running?"

Another fucking question?!

That was the only opening I needed to vent my pent-up frustrations. To me, the experiment of the singles' party was over, and I didn't have to pretend anymore. The party smile was gone. RBF reactivated.

"Where am I running?" I snapped at him, not losing my stride. "To my car, to get out of here! I can't believe I actually came to one of these things. All you men, you're all the same. You all want the same thing from a woman. All of you—same thing! Marriage and kids! Am I right?" I stopped walking and confronted him face-to-face. "Do you want to get married and have kids? Ugh? Do you?! Do you want to get married and have kids?!"

Without missing a beat, he replied, "How 'bout we start with coffee?"

He made me laugh. It disarmed me. When I really looked at him, I saw this lovely man in front of me. He was approximately six feet tall, in good shape with rugged good looks, a warm smile, and kind eyes. It had been a long time since a man looked at me with kindness in his eyes. I liked it. I needed it. My mood softened.

"Sorry. Guess I freaked out a little."

"Hey, I get it. These things are a necessary evil," he said. We talked for a while and he asked if he could take me to dinner. I gave him my phone number.

That was Saturday. He didn't call Sunday. Monday came and went. My friend Victoria said he'd call by Tuesday. My other friend Stephanie said Wednesday was the official deadline to ask for a date that weekend. On Thursday, Mitch, my male friend from high school, lectured me about giving out my home number. Friday I took my son to college, and Saturday Eric called. He asked me to dinner for Wednesday. I said Thursday would be better. After all, he made me wait a week.

We had decided to meet halfway between his city apartment and my suburban townhouse. He suggested we meet at Maggiano's in the Old Orchard Shopping Mall in Skokie. Well, actually, in the bar of Maggiano's in the Old Orchard Shopping Mall in Skokie. And I wondered, *Is this a test? Does dinner depend on how well cocktails go?*

I arrived early, so I stood off in a corner out of sight and watched when he rushed in, looked around, ordered a beer, and waited at a table. That was my cue. I took a deep breath and jumped into the dating world.

He told me how brave I was to meet a total stranger. That sparked the memory of a conversation I just had with my twenty-four-year-old agent.

"Did you hear about this form of genital herpes that's going around? It's transmitted by the slightest contact, and if you've been with more than three people, you have a one hundred percent chance of getting it. I'm considering celibacy."

I had no idea why I thought discussing herpes was proper cocktail conversation.

Luckily the hostess interrupted to tell us our table was ready. I guess he found he could talk to me about anything, and our dinner conversation flowed nonstop. He had majored in film and television in college; I'd majored in theatre. He went off to New York and worked as a production assistant; I became a commercial actress and relied on production assistants. He loved the city; I was born in the city and longed to move back.

I was in the moment with him and enjoyed myself. I loved the way his eyes fixated on me during our conversation. I remembered; I do like men. Some of them are nice. Some of them are trustworthy. Some of them appreciate women. I felt like I was out with one of the good ones.

The waiter took our half-eaten dinners and asked if we wanted them wrapped in one or two take-home bags. I stared at the waiter wondering what he meant. I had been married for twenty years and was always given one take-home bag because we went home together. I assumed that was the question I was being asked: *Are you going home with him?* I panicked and screamed at the waiter, "TWO!"

Although my scream caused the entire restaurant to pause for a brief second, I wasn't embarrassed. I leaned back in my chair, looked at Eric across the table, and asked, "How's that for taking the mystery out of the way this evening's gonna wind up for you?"

"You're funny." His broad grin told me that kind of flirtation was appreciated.

It was all so new to me. I hadn't been single in my twenties and thirties and didn't get a chance to discover who I was or what I was like on my own. That night I learned I was witty and funny. *Who knew?* I was pretty pleased with those discoveries.

After dinner we went for a walk. Then he escorted me to my car, where he kissed me goodnight. The kiss was soft and tender and then he kissed me again, holding it just a little longer, and then one last time where his tongue, ever … so … slightly grazed mine … It sent an unexpected current throughout my whole body. My forty-year-old hormones woke up and began singing, *Do me do me do…* Then he started to leave. *LEAVE?*

He turned and said, "I'd like to see you again, soon."

Now, I had been married my whole adult life, and a kiss like that meant sex was imminent. On the outside I was calm and managed, "I'd like that." But as I watched him walk away, I felt like Demi Moore in the movie *Disclosure* when she yelled at Michael Douglas to *get back here and finish what you started!*

The whole way home I was shocked and amazed. I never expected to feel *those* feelings, especially on a first date. So, in addition to learning that I was witty and funny, did I also just discover that I could be a one-night stand? Was I turning into one of those fast girls Mother warned me that boys don't respect? I was totally confused and in desperate need of the updated rules. But one thing, one thing I knew for sure—I definitely had to rethink the celibacy thing!

"Rethink the Celibacy Thing" was taken from a chapter in **Judi Lee Goshen**'s soon to be released book, *Fornicationally Challenged*, which was originally a stage production directed by Mark Travis. It ran in Los Angeles and New York.

Judi is an actress, writer, and storyteller. She first appeared on stage at seventeen, was an Improv performer in her twenties, and her thirties were spent doing dozens of national TV commercials. Most recently, she portrayed a doctor on Chicago Med.

A storyteller since 1999, she's performed at The Moth, Story Sessions, Chicago Solo, Story Jam, Solo in the Second City, Celtic Knot, Upright Citizen's Brigade, That's All She Wrote, Do Not Submit, Arlene Malinowski's Speak Easy, This Much Is True, Homewood Stories, Tellin' Tales Theater, Loose Chicks, Soul Stories Live, and Story Salon in Los Angeles.

Her comedic postmarital dating memoir, Fornicationally Challenged: My Reluctant Return to Dating, is now available on Amazon.

Judi has a Fiction Writing degree from Columbia College. In her day job, she works for the University of Chicago. On the weekends, she plays with her grandchildren.

ACKNOWLEDGEMENTS

There are many people who made this book possible. The first person we want to thank is Jill Howe who wrote the Foreword and who started Friends with Words, which has brought a community of writers together and garnered true and lasting friendships. Jill has continued to be an inspiring example of how much one person can get done—from facilitating workshops for writers to creating storytelling shows all while working full time.

We also want to thank our very talented contributors who make this book funny, heartwarming and meaningful. It was a pleasure to work with all of you. We are grateful that you have shared a part of yourself on the page: David Barish, Kevin Biolsi, Ellen Blum-Barish, Margaret Burk, Jonathan Euseppi, Steve Glickman, John Hahm, Jesse Hall, Lynne Jordan, Michael Jered Kopp, Arlene Malinowski, Ericka McFee, Lindsey Monroe-Bougher, Pamela Morgan, Marya Morris, JH Palmer, Carmenita Peoples, Sheri Reda, Victoria Reeves, Stephanie Rogers, Anna Tuccoli, Debbi Welch, and the late (deeply missed) Tom Wolferman. You all wanted to create something that would be a testament to the great storytelling community in Chicago.

Last, we want to thank our editor, Diane Telgen for her contribution to this book. She is a stickler for correct punctuation, grammar and adherence to the Chicago Manual of Style. Her attention to detail is reflected in this book everywhere.

And thank you, reader, for picking up this volume.

ABOUT THE EDITOR

Judi Lee Goshen

Judi is an actress, writer, and storyteller. She first appeared on stage at seventeen, was an Improv performer in her twenties, and her thirties were spent doing dozens of national TV commercials. Most recently, she portrayed a doctor on Chicago Med.

A storyteller since 1999, she's told at The Moth, Story Sessions, Chicago Solo, Story Jam, Solo in the Second City, Celtic Knot, Upright Citizen's Brigade, That's All She Wrote, Do Not Submit, Arlene Malinowski's Speak Easy, This Much Is True, Homewood Stories, Tellin' Tales Theater, Loose Chicks, Soul Stories Live, and Story Salon in Los Angeles.

Her comedic postmarital dating memoir, "Fornicationally Challenged: My Reluctant Return to Dating," is available on Amazon.

Judi has a Fiction Writing degree from Columbia College. In her day job, she works for the University of Chicago. On the weekends, she plays with her grandchildren.

ABOUT THE EDITOR

Anne E. Beall, PhD

Anne is a writer and storyteller who has published nine books on a variety of topics. She was recently interviewed on NPR about her book Heroic, Helpful & Caring Cats, and her book Cinderella Didn't Live Happily Ever After was featured in People Magazine. She has told stories all over Chicago in a variety of shows, including Story Lab, Ten by Nine, Is This a Thing, Soul Stories, and The Moth.

Her other books include: 5-Minute Sleep Meditations; 5-Minute Meditation Vacations; Community Cats, Heartfelt Connections: How Animals & People Help One Another; Strategic Market Research; Reading the Hidden Communications Around You; and The Psychology of Gender.

She is the CEO and founder of Beall Research, a strategic market research firm. Originally from Massachusetts, she's lived in Chicago for over twenty years and enjoys walking on the lakefront, sampling dark beers, and listening to other storytellers.

BOOKS BY THIS AUTHOR

5-Minute Sleep Meditations: Fantasy Journeys With An Inspirational Message

So many of us struggle to fall asleep. The second our heads hit the pillow, our minds race through lengthy to-do lists, work problems, and the latest news. How do you wipe it all away so you can fall asleep? Psychologist Anne Beall's 5-Minute Sleep Meditations: Fantasy Journeys with a Personal Message helps readers forget their worries, relax, and fall into a wonderful slumber. With over twenty-five guided meditations, this book takes readers on fantasy journeys to secret gardens, enchanted tree houses, and other imaginary worlds where they meet intelligent creatures, travel through time, and commune with nature. Each meditation leaves readers with an inspiring message that leads them to a state of tranquility: "You are one of the world's perfect creatures," "Your life is a wonderful adventure," "Relax and let your body go," are just some of the messages within. The Dalai Lama, experts at the Mayo Clinic, and even Oprah, tout meditation as a way to restore calm, bring inner peace, and improve sleep. Whether you're suffering from difficulty falling asleep, unwelcome awakenings, or an on-going sleep disorder, these nightly readings can prepare you for a deep and restful night's sleep. For more 5-Minute Meditations, see Beall's 5-Minute Meditation Vacations: Magical Journeys with a Personal Message.

5-Minute Meditation Vacations: Magical Journeys With A Personal Message

Take a 5-minute break, get away and relax. Suspend disbelief and find yourself in a magical garden or on a luxurious yacht with friends or in a hot-air balloon. You're the main character in each journey where you take a trip and receive a message at the end. Each journey is magical and you may receive your message in any number of ways. Take a short trip in your mind, visit a new place, relieve some stress, and get an insight at the end. This version has color photographs.

Heroic, Helpful & Caring Cats: Felines Who Make A Difference

Dogs have masters; cats have staff. That old saying reflects the conventional wisdom about our favorite pets. Cats are described as independent and aloof. But that stereotype clashes with the reality of untold cat companions, who know that their felines can be just as affectionate, devoted, and trainable as any dog. Like Basil, a licensed therapist who comforts hospital patients and staff, hospice-care residents, and trauma victims. Or Belle, who repaid being rescued from a sewer in Costa Rica by becoming a devoted nurse to her companion during his lengthy illness. Or Peach, who can run obstacle courses, play a piano, and perform other amazing advanced tricks. Or the dozens of stray and feral cats who have inspired their caretakers to step up and become involved, hands-on advocates within their communities. These are just some of the real-life cat stories that animal advocate and psychologist Anne Beall shares in Heroic, Helpful, & Caring Cats. These heartwarming stories highlight how cats can comfort, inspire, and connect with the humans they love. Including Beall's original cat research into American attitudes towards their furry friends, this book reveals the depths of connection and empathy people and cats can share. Read Heroic, Helpful, & Caring Cats to learn about cat psychology, and discover what feline fans have always known: if you want unconditional love, adopt a cat.

Heartfelt Connections: How Animals And People

Help One Another

What is the nature of the connection between people and animals? Or, put another way, how do the relationships that form between humans and our animal companions have profound influences on our lives? From beloved family companions to therapy animals, search and rescue canines, and other animals who help their human partners heal, learn, and grow, there are compelling reasons to believe that animals and people are inextricably and deeply connected to one another. In Heartfelt Connections: How Animals and People Help One Another, author and social psychologist Anne E. Beall explores the relationships that occur between humans and animals, and she describes the many people whose lives have been changed tremendously by animals. With stories and research about horses who heal, dogs who help children read, cats who save the lives of their owners, and pigs, sheep, ducks, and llamas who help reduce stress and lift the spirits of people, Beall shows how animals are in action across the United States at nursing homes, at hospitals, and at rehabilitation centers and are making a difference in the lives of many people. Beall finds that even a household pet can make people feel better about the world and about themselves, and these pets can also provide comfort and friendship in times of need. And as therapy and rehabilitation animals help victims of abuse, trauma, and even war overcome their own challenges, the bond between humans and animals grows even stronger--a deep connection that is truly heartfelt.

Community Cats: A Journey Into The World Of Feral Cats

It all started when a rat ran over a family member's foot and Dr. Anne E. Beall began a journey into the world of feral cats. Beall had experienced rat problems for a long time. Then a neighbor told her about a program called Cats at Work, where one could get feral cats that would take care of the rat problem.In Community

Cats, she tells how she entered the world of feral cats when she signed up for the Chicago Cats at Work program with Tree House Humane Society. Tree House practices TNVR (trap-neuter-vaccinate-return), and they trapped, neutered, vaccinated, and relocated a feral cat colony to Beall's home. She narrates what she learned about the unique world of feral cats and about the people who are involved with feral cats and who advocate for them.Community Cats shares the story of what initially began as a creative solution to a rat problem and became a journey that led her to reach out to others in the feral-cat world. Beall interviewed other colony caretakers and leaders in the TNVR movement and learned about how feral cats live, how they relate to one another, and how they relate to their caretakers. She also conducted survey research on Americans attitudes toward stray cats, TNVR programs, and spaying/neutering.Beall learned that feral-cat programs have a huge impact on the caretakers of the colonies, on the neighbors, on the community, and on the cats themselves, and she details those findings in Community Cats.

Cinderella Didn't Live Happily Ever After: The Hidden Messages In Fairy Tales

Did Cinderella live happily ever after? You might think so until you look more closely at the hidden messages in beloved fairy tales. In this book, fairy tales are analyzed in terms of the underlying messages about marriage, agency, power, suffering, and good versus evil, with a focus on how male and female characters differ in each of these areas. The analysis is a data-driven approach that provides clear evidence for the hidden messages in these beloved tales. The end conclusion is not whether fairy tales are good or bad but rather what messages they deliver about life, even if unintentionally.

Reading The Hidden Communications Around You: A Guide To Reading Body Language In The

Workplace

How well do you read the body language of the people around you? Researchers estimate that nonverbal communication comprises between 60 to 93 percent of all communication. How much are you missing? In Reading the Hidden Communications Around You, author Anne Beall shares her approach to reading customers and colleagues. Beall describes an easy, intuitive way to interpret body language called PERCEIVE, a technique Beall developed after an exhaustive review of relevant academic studies conducted in the fields of psychology, anthropology, and communication. PERCEIVE can be used to identify receptivity, like, dislike, discomfort, stress, deception and emotions. It can also be used for impression management to increase perceptions of credibility, trustworthiness and likability in the workplace. Beall provides insight into the major aspects of nonverbal communication, including facial expressions, physical contact, eyes, gestures and voice, as well as proximity and relative orientation, which are the foundation of body language.With real-life examples and photos, Reading the Hidden Communications Around You helps you observe nonverbal behavior, use the PERCEIVE method to read peoples reactions and emotions, and present an appropriate response for each situation.

Strategic Market Research: A Guide To Conducting Research That Drives Businesses

For a company to embrace market research as a facilitator of change, it must be willing to take the approach that makes the most impact on its organization. In this guide, author Anne Beall shares her unique approach for conducting strategic market research. With more than 25 years of experience, Beall details the strategic principles she has developed that impact the way in which market research can inspire and change an organization. It all begins with the following steps: Identifying the strategic questions that will help a business; Using the right research techniques to answer these questions; Obtaining the level of depth required to have insight; Reading the nonverbal communications of research respondents; Identifying the emotional aspects of human behavior; Using statistical analyses to understand what drives markets; Going beyond the data to interpret the results and make strategic recommendations. In addition to addressing both qualitative and quantitative research, Strategic Market Research provides real-life examples illustrating the application of these concepts in various scenarios, including businesses and non-profit organizations.

Fornicationally Challenged: My Reluctant Return To Dating

Judi was married when she should have been single, and single when she should have been married (but don't say that on a first date if you're hoping for a second). Freshly out of an oppressive marriage at forty, Judi's plan of celibacy is thwarted by the raging hormones of her sexual prime. Haunted by her dead Jewish mother and armed with only the Surgeon General's warning about safe-sex practices and her best friend's snarky advice, she dates a series of men who all dump her just before consummating the relationship. Eventually she finds love with a younger man but faces the risk of being silenced once again. Adapted from her successful solo show, Fornicationally Challenged is a twenty-year journey of self-discovery, one man at a time.

THANK YOU AND FEEDBACK

Dear Reader,

Thank you so much for spending your time reading this book. We hope that you enjoyed these stories and found the tellers inspiring.

If you have feedback about the book, you can email us at Hello@ChicagoStoryPress.com. Whether you loved it or hated it, tell us what you think.

Finally, if you have a few minutes, it would help tremendously if you reviewed this book.

Reviews make a huge difference, and the more reviews a book receives, the more people will learn about it.

Thanks again,

Anne E. Beall & Judi Lee Goshen

Made in USA - Kendallville, IN
1200924_9780578806280
12 08 2020 1949